SONG FOR A POOR BOY

By The Same Author :

HEART OF GRACE (*Linden Press.* London)
CHRIST IN LONDON (*Linden Press,* London)
THE WOOD-BURNERS (*New Writers Press,* Dublin)
MAN ON THE PORCH (*Martin Brian and O'Keeffe,* London)
FOLK TALES FOR THE GENERAL (*Raven Arts Press,* Dublin)

Plays : Three plays published by THRESHOLD - Lyric Theatre, Belfast.

SONG FOR A POOR BOY

A CORK CHILDHOOD

Patrick Galvin

Raven Arts Press/Dublin

SONG FOR A POOR BOY
is first published in 1990 by
The Raven Arts Press
P.O. Box 1430
Finglas
Dublin 11
Ireland

ISBN 1 85186 080 0

Raven Arts Press receives financial assistance from The Arts Council (An Chomhairle Ealaíon), Dublin, Ireland.

Acknowledgements are due to *THE CORK EXAMINER, CYPHERS, THE IRISH NEWS* and *IRELAND OF THE WELCOMES*. Also to the BBC (Radio 4) who broadcast extracts from this volume.

Designed by Dermot Bolger and Aidan Murphy, cover design by Rapid Productions. Photograph courtesy of The Cork Examiner.

Printed in Ireland by Colour Books Ltd, Baldoyle

SONG FOR A POOR BOY

For my parents

SONG FOR A POOR BOY

When he was young he had no sense
And souls were sold for eighteen pence
While he ran mad in streets of gold
And people said he must be old
And hard as nails.

When hunger tore the windows out
And all the rooms were steeped in sin
He prayed to witches in his bed
And painted all the door knobs red
And danced and sang.

But sticks and stones came tumbling down
When he put on his royal gown
And overright the convent wall
We dressed him in his mother's shawl
And broke his back.

And strong men went to take his soul
When he refused his begging bowl
But he was made to stretch his wings
And lead a company of kings
And touch the stars.

And silver ghosts leapt from his hand
When famine raged across the land
We locked him in a padded cell
And said he'd surely go to hell
And twist and burn.

But in the dark he learned to creep
When all the guards were fast asleep
And in his house of spinning pearls
We hopped about in loops and whirls
And rang the bell.

Patrick Galvin

We chained him to the madhouse floor
And heard his long night goblin's roar
He split the chain and smashed the lock
And stopped the white wall ticking clock
And climbed the stair.

We held him down inside his tomb
We robbed his heart and fired his room
He watched us from his bony place
And all the seas ran down his face
And drained the world.

But when the lamps were going down
He made himself a one-eyed clown
He saw the sun fall through the skies
And knew that all we knew was lies -
And grinned and grinned.

1

The house we lived in had a grey-brick face. A large tenement close to the Lee. Come Spring tides, the river overflowed its banks, water rose in the streets and in our bare feet we paddled out our lives. Good lives. Spring-awakening lives — splashing wildly through cobbled streets and saving pennies for Bull's Eyes, Frog's Eyes and Annie's Gudge — a pudding-like cake sold by the slab and guaranteed to contain only the finest ingredients grown specially in foreign climes.

My friend, Connors, hated Gudge. He said it had been trampled on by natives. But he shared mine and when we'd finished eating we sat down and listened to the wireless.

For, sure enough, we had a wireless. A crystal-set with cat's whiskers. And if you listened carefully through both earphones you could hear music and laughter till the battery ran out.

Then you had to change it. Top it up with burning acid or pure still water — or whatever it was that the man did down in the bicycle shop and charged you twopence. He sold bicycles too, but he was known as The Battery Man and you could taste his genius. A man who could bring music out of the air and laughter into the living-room. The music was magic and the laughter was funny — though we seldom managed to see the joke. Maybe it was foreign.

But then, everything was foreign that existed beyond the North Gate Bridge — and we lived on the South Side. The old Cork. The real Cork and none of your blow-ins.

My Grand-parents, on my mother's side, were born there and their Grand-parents before them. And you could trace them back to when Cork was only a marsh and maybe even before that. My grandmother said so. She lived to be eighty-nine and never once crossed the North Gate Bridge.

"Tis unknown the kind of people who'd be living over there. Bogmen and Shite-hawks who came in from beyond the lamps years ago with nothing to their feet but cow dung. Keep well away from them."

And so I did. Though my father said that my Grandmother had a screw loose and 'twas no wonder her husband ran away

9

from her and ended up dead in America.

My Grandfather did end up dead in America, but my Grandmother said it couldn't have happened to a better man. My Grandmother didn't like men. She said they should be preserved in bottles.

When she was sixteen years of age, my Grandmother married Mick O'Leary. He was a fisherman who never fished beyond the limits of Evergreen Street. And when he married my Grandmother and was persuaded to move to Barrack Street he was convinced that he'd settled abroad. He was happy enough, but he would have preferred to remain at home.

I never met Mick O'Leary, but his photograph stood upon the mantelpiece in my Grandmother's house in Barrack Street. It was covered in dust, and the eyes peered through a mist and followed you everywhere.

On Sundays, when I went to visit my Grandmother, I would ask her about Mick, but she was reluctant to talk about him. And when I suggested that it might be a good idea to wipe the dust off the photograph she said "the dust suits him". The remainder of the house was free of dust. She cleaned it meticulously.

When Mick married my Grandmother he was proud to give her his name. My Grandmother told him to keep it. Moll Delaney was her name and no scrap of paper was going to deprive her of her true identity. Moll was proud of her identity, proud of herself, and had little respect for marriage. Why she married Mick O'Leary is unknown, and when I was once bold enough to ask her she said "I was astray in the head". I could never imagine my Grandmother being astray in the head. She knew what she was doing and her mind was as sharp as a butcher's blade.

Two years after their marriage, my Grandmother gave birth to my mother. She was their only child and my Grandmother insisted that she be baptised in both their names. My mother was in no position to argue the matter at the time, but when it came to her turn to marry my father, she called herself Bridget O'Brien — which confused everybody, including herself.

My Grandmother smiled. She never liked the Galvins anyway and when I went to visit her for the first time in my youth she said that I wasn't a Galvin at all and that my proper name was Sweeney. I called myself Sweeney for a time, but gave it up when

10

I discovered that Sweeney was a mad poet who lived in a tree and had nothing to eat for breakfast but pine nuts and tree-bark.

Sometimes, my Grandmother could be less confusing. One day, she looked at me and said "Chicago". I had never heard of Chicago. "It's in America" she said. And I waited.

"That's where he went. Mick. Went raving mad one day in the middle of Barrack Street and said he was going to Chicago. Go to hell, I said. And off he went."

"I thought you said that he never ventured beyond the bottom of Barrack Street?"

"He didn't. I told you. He went mad suddenly. Left me and your mother and jumped on to the boat. Give him his due, he did ask me to go with it, but I wouldn't leave Cork."

"Why not, Grandma?"

"Don't ask stupid questions, Child. And don't call me Grandma. People who call me Grandma end up in a madhouse where they get tortured by Sister Mary. You know Sister Mary, don't you?"

"No."

"Well, you soon will do if you don't watch yourself. I used to tell Mick to watch himself. But he took no notice — and look what happened to him. Shot dead in Chicago. Bootlegging.

"What's bootlegging?"

"Ask that thing you call your father. He's probably an expert. Mick was just wanting. They sent me a telegram when he died, but I threw it on the fire."

The eyes peered from the photograph on the mantelpiece and my Grandmother lapsed into silence. I wondered why Mick had gone mad suddenly and run off to Chicago. She refused to explain. She was like that. Nothing to explain. Her life was her own. She worked hard and gave thanks to no one.

"I took in washing. I plucked chickens. I had a black shawl and the feathers covered it."

I remembered the black shawl and I remembered the feathers. They clung to the soft black wool like snowflakes that would never melt. She tried to wash the shawl. She spent hours picking the feathers off with her fingers and her teeth, but they held fast — a constant reminder of hard work and eternal fortitude.

She was eighty-nine when she died. The room tidied. Everything in its place. The fire set in the grate. Only the photograph on the mantelpiece remained covered with dust. And Mick O'Leary's eyes followed her into death.

2

When I was seven years of age my mother held my hand and walked me to school for the first time.

"I want you to be educated," she said.

I had no intention of being educated. The schoolroom stifled me. The educating air was filled with chalk and the heavy slate blackboard screeched whenever Brother Reynolds wrote on it.

Brother Reynolds was a big man — light on his feet and, sometimes, light in the head. He taught English to Irishmen. And every day he would read aloud from *The Ballad Of Reading Jail*. He never mentioned the author.

I remember the line. "For each man kills the thing he loves." Brother Reynolds must have loved me to distraction. He kept hitting me over the head with a ruler. He was dying to educate me and said it would be a miracle if he succeeded.

I was a great believer in miracles, but I did not believe they could be found in a classroom. And Brother Reynolds was not like my father or my mother — or my Grandmother or my mad Aunt Bridget. They were miracles.

When my father was unemployed and my mother scrubbed floors for a living — that was a miracle. Her strength held us. Her gentle hands cradled us in miracles.

When my father played music — that was a miracle. The music flowed from the dreams in his head and you could see it dancing on the tips of his fingers as he touched the holes in that shimmering instrument.

We dined on miracles. We found them at home and in the streets and we found them on the East roof of Saint Finbarr's cathedral. A golden angel stood there waiting to proclaim the ending of the world. Cork would be favoured. Seven years before the last trumpet-sound the angel would turn green. We kept our eyes on the angel. And through summer days and summer nights he watched over us.

When Autumn came and the leaves fell from the trees along the Mardyke we sat as lovers in Fitzgerald's Park and kissed and kissed and promised never to tell a single soul or her father would kill her stone dead and bury her in a bottle. On our way

13

home we stared hard at the angel — searching anxiously for signs of green. There were none. Our golden angel still shone and glittered over the city.

You could see its reflection on the waters of the Lee. You could feel its presence in the South Presentation Convent where Brother Reynolds struggled to educate us. And here was the final miracle — we survived his efforts and exploded through the oak doors every afternoon when school was over for another day.

There was freedom in the streets. Freedom to wander through the English and Irish markets where everything was sold — from rare spices to secondhand clothes. You could smell the spices, feel the texture of Chinese silk and dream of ships that sailed the seas in search of treasures for the people of Cork. On stormy nights we knelt at home and prayed hard for poor sailors at sea.

When Winter came my father lit the oil lamp, raised the fire in the hearth and took down his tin whistle from its place above the mantelpiece. He played "The Croppy Boy" and "Erin's Lovely Lee" and my mother sang "The Rookery".

The neighbours came in. They climbed the stairs to our tenement flat and sat on the floor and sang and told stories. Mr Cotter played the flute and Salty Cleary said that at one time Ireland was ruled entirely by women and he could prove it.

Didn't his father tell him one time of a woman who was washed up by the sea near Roche's Point and she was fifty feet tall from her shoulders to her feet and her chest was seven feet across and her head was cut off and it was in this way she was cast up by the sea ? Oh yes, it was true enough and no one could deny it.

My mother smiled — and even my Grandmother smiled. For she believed it and said it was a great pity that things had changed for the worst. My father, as usual, said little. He spoke through his music.

In a corner of the room with a cat named Tone I sat and listened. My father didn't like Tone and sometimes called him Wolfe, but said it was nothing political. He just didn't like cats.

In later years my father became an ardent Free Stater. My mother a staunch Republican. But that was a long way off and I was young and dreamed of growing up. I didn't know then what growing-up was all about. The music filled the memories of my room and I slept innocently.

3

I remember the beginning. The pink and amber of my mother's womb and then the dark and dying of the light. The room was grey. And my first words, on being evicted into this world were —" I shall return!"

When my father was informed of this rather unexpected outburst from a child still attached to the umbilical cord he said "that boy will be a poet". What my father did not know was that I was already a poet.

Sitting there in the comfort of my mother's womb I had already written some of the finest poems in the English language — to say nothing of Greek and the odd spot of Latin. My mother was not aware of all this activity going on inside her. Had she been so she would not have been in such a hurry to evict me. My mother respected poets. She knew that they required warmth, tenderness and compassion — and she knew that such things would be in short supply in Margaret Street.

I emerged roaring. My mother lay on the double bed and my father stood over her and stared at what she'd brought forth.

"He looks odd," he said.

"What do you mean — odd? He's a poet, isn't he? You said that yourself."

"I did. And may the tongue be struck out of me. The country is full of poets. And here's you adding another one to our woes."

"You'll be proud of him yet." said my mother. But my father was not convinced. He loved poetry, but he couldn't stand poets.

"I never met one who wasn't a pauper" he said. "A prey to bailifs, lawyers and priests. Take my advice and send him back."

But my mother never sent anything back. I was her loving child and she held me close to her breast and smiled.

I was happy there. I felt soulful and poetic. I regretted the loss of my mother's womb and of all the poems I had written inside her. But everything happened so quickly that I had no time to collect the manuscripts — and there they remain in three languages protected with love.

When my Grandmother arrived to view the new arrival she said I didn't look like a poet. And when my mother asked her what I did look like she said she'd prefer not to say. I ignored my Grandmother. There was a mad drop in her somewhere and she had no sense of the occasion.

I looked at my father and held fast to my mother. Her breath was warm. Her mouth was gentle — and in spite of my regrets I felt there'd be some compensations. I would be breast-fed for one thing and that could last for years. Poets do well on breast-feeding. Our literature owes much to it.

I moved in closer. I could see myself writing poems about breast-feeding and dedicating them to mothers everywhere. I bit hard and was promptly slapped on the bottom. That slap on the bottom gave me amnesia. I forgot I was a poet and it took me twenty-three years to rediscover my true vocation.

4

Being normal in some respects I did have a Paternal Grandmother. Her name was Lizzie Baron. She was not born in Cork and neither was my Grandfather. He was a Kinsale man. But sometime during the latter half of the nineteenth century he decided that he'd had enough of small seaside towns and set off for the Continent in search of a war. What my Grandfather knew about the Continent of Europe wouldn't cover the back of a postage stamp, but the little he did know was enough to convince him that there must be a war going on out there somewhere.

Whether he found his war or not is one of the great mysteries of our time, but five years later he returned to Cork bearing what he described as a Greek wife — whom he claimed to have rescued from a band of maurading Turks.

My Paternal Grandmother — for that's who she turned out to be — didn't look like a Greek — or a Turk for that matter — but my Grandfather said she was. And since he stood seven feet high in his stocking feet and had a fist on him like a sledge-hammer there seemed little point in arguing the matter. Greek she was — and in due course she mananaged to produce six children, including my father. She also, incidentally, gave birth to my Aunt Bridget. But Bridget went mad at the age of forty. So no one mentioned her, if they could possibly avoid it.

Lizzie, on the other hand, never went mad. Maybe because she was small and dark and quite unlike my Grandfather. Or maybe because her English was bad and sounded like a tin can scraping on a wall. Either way, she remained remarkably sane, sat quietly in a corner, and smiled only when my Grandfather smiled.

Sometimes, of course, she moved out of the corner and went shopping in the English market. My grandfather gave her eight shillings a week from his old age pension and when she returned from her shopping she still retained the eight shillings. My Grandfather said she was the greatest

17

housekeeper in Ireland and I was duly impressed. But my mother said she hadn't paid for a thing and was known far and wide as the "South Side Bandit."

Be that as it may, my Grandfather seemed totally unaware of her reputed exploits and I doubt whether anyone had the courage to tell him. Had they done so he would have anointed them. For he was convinced that my Grandmother was a saint and went to his grave offering up novenas for her eventual canonisation.

Alas, however, for the vageries of Rome. For the Pope either forgot to canonise Lizzie or he was bigoted against the Greeks. Either way, we are still waiting.

One morning, Lizzie rose from her bed and made my Grandfather his usual breakfast of thick porridge and strong black tea. "It's the way he likes it" she said."Strong enough to trot a mouse on." Having completed her task she called to my Grandfather, but there was no response.

She approached the bed and stared down at him. My Grandfather was dead. He had died in his sleep hours before. And though Lizzie had lain beside him all night she was unaware of his passing. She touched his face. The body was still warm, but the light had gone out of it.

She moved away and sat close to the fire. She heard the clock ticking on the mantelpiece and the kettle boiling for a second time on the hob. She ignored the sound and sat there for a long time before informing the neighbours.

When the neighbours arrived, the women stripped my Grandfather of his nightshirt and cap and then washed his body from head to toe. Mr. Cotter shaved him. And when he was cleaned and stretched the women dressed him again. But this time in his long brown habit that he would wear unto eternity.

Outside the room, my father and I sat on the stairs and my father wept. It was the first time I had seen him cry and he would never cry outwardly again. He would retreat into his music.

But now he bled. His shoulders sagged and his body trembled. He buried his face in the palms of his hands and he became an old man.

I would like to have spoken with my father then. I would like to have asked him to explain my Grandfather's death — as he had explained so many other things that had frightened and confused me. But it was not the time and the tears in his eyes told me so.

He had said at one time, when a neighbour died after a long illness, that death was nothing to be afraid of. It was there from the moment of our birth and remained beside us all the days of our lives. It was not dark. It was bright. And when we died we became part of it — a moving into the light. A friendly call from the Creator of all things. It did not seem like that now and I wondered if he still believed it.

"We should be going in now" he said. "It's time we paid our respects to your Grandfather."

We entered the room. The neighbours stood at the foot of the bed and Lizzie sat beside it. She had covered the mattress with a clean white sheet and my Grandfather lay stretched upon it with his hands clapsed in front of him and the grey Connemara rosary beads entwined between his fingers.

My father raised me up.

"Kiss your Grandfather goodbye" he said. And lowered me down towards my Grandfather's lips. I kissed the corpse. I was eight years old. And I knew that death was not friendly. Nor a moving into the light. It was a freezing of the soul. A nightmare of ice that followed me down the years.

5

A year after my Grandfather's death I met Mannie Goldman. Mannie lived in The Marsh, the poorest part of the city, and earned his living writing letters for people who couldn't write themselves. Halfpenny a page, envelopes free, bring your own stamp. I knocked on Mannie's door.

"Go away!"

I opened the door and fell headlong over a pile of books.

"Stupid Boy! Do you realise what you've done? The entire history of the Roman Empire lies hidden in there."

"I'm sorry, Mr. Goldman. But there's no light."

"That's your bad luck. At my age I don't need a light. Sit down."

"Where, Mr. Goldman?"

"There! Beside you. Jane Austen. Sit on her."

I sat on Jane Austen. My first contact with creative literature. Mr. Goldman lit a candle.

"Can you see now?"

"I think so, Mr. Goldman."

Mr Goldman lived in two rooms and they were both filled, from floor to ceiling, with books. They lined the walls, blocked out the windows, covered the floor and lay scattered over the bed. And apart from the bed, the only furniture Mr. Goldman possessed was a chair and a table which he never used except to lay books on.

When Mr. Goldman wanted to sit — he sat on the Oxford Dictionary — all twenty-seven volumes of it, arranged to look like a throne. And when Mr. Goldman wanted something to rest his arm on, he chose the *Collected Proust*.

It's perfectly flat. One of the best editions available. I strongly recommend it.

Any money that Mr. Goldman received from the letter-writing business, he spent on books. And when his cousin in America sent him five pounds every Christmas, he spent that on books. I never saw Mr. Goldman eat. He fed on books.

"My wife left me. Do you know that? Couldn't stand the

books. That woman was obsessed with furniture. She wanted sideboards in here. Mahogany wardrobes. Chairs, if you don't mind! Do you realise that furniture is a myth? It exists when you're there, but the moment you leave the room the furniture disappears. My wife couldn't understand that. Do you?"

"No, Mr. Goldman."

"I'm surrounded by peasants. What do you want?"

"I came to ask you about Nano Nagle, Mr. Goldman."

"Nano Nagle? You mean that female who built the South Presentation Convent? What about her? She's dead isn't she?"

"I know that, Mr. Goldman. But last night I saw her walking up and down Margaret Street. And when I asked my father about that, he said she was in Heaven."

"So?"

"Well, if she's in Heaven — how come she's still walking up and down Margaret Street?"

"Split personality, said Mr. Goldman. Have you read Freud?"

"Was he a Catholic, Mr. Goldman?"

Mr. Goldman almost had a stroke. No — he was not a flaming Catholic. But one of these days that Pope of yours is going to canonise him. Ask me why? Go on — ask me why!

"Why, Mr. Goldman?"

"That's a damned good question. I'm glad you asked me. Well, before Freud came along the Catholic Church was just about getting ready to abandon the concept of Original Sin. Then along comes Freud and hands the whole thing back to them in the form of a guilt complex. Do you understand what I mean?"

I didn't. And Mr Goldman knew that I didn't. He shook his head.

"How old are you?"

"Nine."

"Are you going to school?"

"Yes."

"So much for education. When I was nine I was reading Dostoevsky. When I was ten I was reading Karl Marx. I understood him better then, than I do now, but that's progress. Can you read?"

"A bit."

"What does that mean — comics?"

"There's big books in school, Mr. Goldman."

"How big? Is there anything in them?"

"I don't know, Mr. Goldman."

"Of course you don't. Who sent you to talk to me?"

"My father."

"Oh. I remember him. I wrote a letter for him one time. He was looking for a job. Did he get it?"

"I don't think so, Mr. Goldman. He's still on the dole."

Mr. Goldman paused. A pity he said. Maybe next time he'll have more luck. You can go now. I've answered your question."

"Split personality."

"That's right. It's quite common among people with religion. Was there something else?"

"No, Mr. Goldman."

"Then off you go."

He turned away. picked up a book and began to read. I moved towards the door and turned the handle.

"Just a minute" he said — and lowered the book he was holding. "I don't know why I'm doing this. I hate children. But if you want to borrow any of these books, you're welcome to do so. But ask your father first. I don't want those lunatics from the Purity League howling for my blood."

I had never heard of the Purity League and I would ask my father. For the books fascinated me. And Mr. Goldman fascinated me as he sat there on the Oxford Dictionary looking like a garden gnome.

"What's going to happen to all those books when you die, Mr. Goldman?"

Mr. Goldman laughed. "Die? Don't be ridiculous! But, if you must know — I've willed them all to my wife. And my one regret is that I won't be around to see her face when the delivery man dumps half a million books on her doorstep."

He laughed again and I forgot about Nano Nagle and why she was walking up and down Margaret Street when she should have been in Heaven. Maybe she didn't like Heaven, or maybe she did have a split personality as Mr. Goldman had said.

I went to visit Mr. Goldman every day after school and sometimes at night. He taught me to read and he taught me to write. And during the long winter evenings, when the rain danced upon those invisible windows in Mr. Goldman's rooms, I sat at his feet while he read aloud from a myriad of books.

Tolstoy and Dostoevsky, Gorky and Emil Zola, Voltaire and Spinoza, Marlow and Blake — Berkeley and Berkeley again —

and for good measure — the ballad history of my native city. He knew it well. His heart made room for it and it would always be there, as he was whenever I needed him.

I remember the room. The sound of his voice. The movement of his hands as he turned the pages. He read until he was tired and slept where he sat — perched high on the Oxford Dictionary.

6

When the Spanish Civil War broke out, Mr. Goldman stood at the corner of Washington Street and protested against the Fascists. My mother supported him and, in the evenings, she painted slogans on our tenement wall urging the natives of Cork to aid the Republicans and join the International Brigades.

My father thought differently. He said that the Republicans were burning the churches in Spain and he didn't want to see anything like that happening in Cork. But he refused to join the Blueshirts, who were marching through the city wearing holy medals, and appealing to the people to join them in their Great Crusade against the Bolsheviks.

At a huge rally in the city, Monsignor Sexton said that twenty-four Sisters of the Poor had been crucified in Barcelona, and when two men asked him for proof, they were thrown into the river Lee and had to be rescued by the Salvation Army.

The Salvation Army said that it was their Christian duty to rescue people from the river Lee and offered to make tea for everybody, if only they'd be sensible and go home. But the crowd didn't go home. They knelt in the streets and prayed for General Franco.

At the corner of Washington Street, Mr. Goldman still stood and protested loudly. My mother brought him a bowl of soup from the Penny Dinner house in Hanover Street, but he refused to eat it. He said he was starving for Spain. She offered to mend a hole in his jacket, too — but he said he was quite capable of doing that himself — though he never did.

He looked weary and old, as if he'd seen it all before and there was little he could do now to prevent it happening again. I wondered where he'd grown-up and about his family background. He never mentioned it.

In the evenings, I sat at his feet and listened to him read. And during the day I attended school and listened to Brother Reynolds talking about Spain. Brother Reynolds knew everything about Spain. He'd read it in the newspapers.

He said that Spain was a Catholic country and the Communists were out to destroy it. He said the Communists were everywhere. But if they were, so was General Franco.

25

His photograph appeared in every newspaper. His eyes peered at you out of every shop window. And his spirit haunted the classroom where Brother Reynolds was telling us that what was happening in Spain to-day could be happening in Ireland to-morrow.

Atrocities were being committed out there. Children were being burned alive by the Reds, and their ashes scattered on pig-farms in Galicia. Priests were being hanged. Bishops were being shot through the eyes. Nuns were being raped. And when my friend, Connors, asked him what rape meant, he split him over the head with a metal ruler and told him to wash his mouth out with salt and then drench himself in holy water. He asked us to pray.

We should pray for General Franco. We should pray for the Moors who were fighting now to save Christianity, we should pray for the Blueshirts and join them to-day and be remembered forever in the Great Book Of Names that was now being prepared in Heaven by Blessed Michael and his angels.

My friend Connors threw up — and others joined the Blueshirts. They danced and they marched and they wore uniforms and looked like Boy Scouts. But when Brother Reynolds saw them he said they were like little angels who would one day grow up to be big angels and then they could fly off to Spain and help General Franco to kill the Reds.

He appealed for money to buy guns. He placed a collection-box at the school gate and said that anyone who failed to contribute would burn in Hell for all Eternity. They would be tortured by demons.

When I told my mother about Brother Reynolds, she said he was a born eegit. But Mr. Goldman said he was only one of many. The country was full of them. My father said nothing, but when he saw the collection box at the school gate, on his way to Mass, he kept his hand in his pocket.

One evening as I sat with Mr. Goldman, listening to him read, someone threw a brick through the window. The shattered glass cascaded across the room and Mr. Goldman flung his coat over my head. We sat in the dark and waited for a second brick. But there was only one — and it was followed by a man's voice shouting "Dirty Jew. You murdered Christ!."

The following day, Mr. Goldman returned to the corner of Washington Street. He continued to protest.

7

In our tenement flat in Margaret Street, my father sat at the window and played the tin whistle. There was a knock at the door and my mother went to answer it. The landlady stood there. You could tell it was Monday.

Mrs. Denton always called on a Monday. She charged three shillings and sixpence a week for two rooms in the attic, and she took a personal interest in collecting the rent.

She entered the room. She carried a black Gladstone bag. She wore a feather in her hat. She had large white teeth and her mouth was full of them.

When Mrs. Denton smiled you could see the graveyards of Cork. And when she nodded her head, you could hear bells tolling for all those who had died clutching her rent books. She smiled now and demanded an extra sixpence off the arrears. My mother paid her four shillings and Mrs. Denton thanked her. She was like that. Always polite when receiving money.

When my father told her that there were rats in the house, Mrs. Denton showed her teeth. She said there were no rats in the house. My father said there were and showed her two dead ones he'd managed to trap in a cage.

Mrs. Denton shook her head. The rats were foreign. They'd come in off the boats on the quays and she could not be held responsible for that. If the rats had been Irish, that would have been a different matter. But they weren't. They came from Japan or China, or some other outlandish place, and what else could you expect? Personally, she was against the whole business of trading with lesser nations and suggested that my father write to the Department Of Foreign Affairs about it. My father said he'd never learned to write and Mrs. Denton said it was a pity, but he was probably better off. Education was a curse and did nothing but give illusions of grandeur to the poor. You couldn't win with Mrs. Denton.

When she was ill, she said that those who were in arrears with their rent had laid a curse on her. And when she recovered, she said God was on her side and no one could harm her. She

27

said the poor were the salt of the Earth — provided they paid their rent and remembered who they were. My mother threw a chair at her — and missed. Mrs. Denton smiled and carried her teeth with her as she descended the stairs.

On the floor below lived the Murphy sisters and their brother, Pat. They were never in arrears because Pat was a member of the Third Order Of Saint Frances and believed it was a mortal sin to owe money. He was the only one in the house who didn't owe money — and he wore his habit every night to keep the ghosts away.

But the ghosts came anyway. They hovered over his bed, waited for him in dark corners, and leapt at him from behind stone walls when he'd had too much to drink, or too little, or none at all. His two sisters said he was massive — their favourite word meaning beautiful. When they saw me in my First Communion suit, they said I looked massive. I did. I always look massive when I'm expecting money.

My cousin Martin was always expecting money. He lived on the second floor back and had a notice in his window saying — "Still expecting. What the hell's keeping ye?" He had a pet dog and the dog followed him everywhere. When the expected money failed to arrive, Martin painted the dog green and tried to sell him in the Coal Quay Market. "Green Dog For Sale. Going Cheap. Just arrived from Ethiopia." There were no offers. The dog relieved himself on the pavement — and Martin spent a month trying to get the paint off with paraffin oil.

On the second floor front lived the Egan family. All mad from eating porridge. Mr. Egan was a docker and a ardent supporter of General Franco. He said my mother was a disgrace and spent most of his time washing off the slogans she'd painted on the wall supporting the Republicans and the International Brigades. My mother replaced the slogans and added "Up Franco — with a bomb!" Mr. Egan got confused. He thought my mother was about to change sides. He said "God moves in mysterious ways." And, for once, my mother was speechless.

When Mr. Egan wasn't busy washing slogans off our tenement wall, he was out collecting jam-jars in Galley's Dump. Mr. Egan liked jam-jars and hated cups. He refused to let any of his family drink from one of them. He preferred jam-jars. And the entire flat creaked under the weight of them. All bound with steel bands to prevent them from exploding when Mrs. Egan

28

poured boiling hot tea into them.

On Sundays, Mr. Egan called the family to order. He paraded them up and down Margaret Street and they all sang "Faith Of Our Fathers" in honour of General Franco. Then they marched to Galley's Dump to collect more jam-jars. Mr. Egan said they were classic, but Mrs. Egan wasn't too sure. She said art was beyond her.

The ground floor flat was occupied by the Sweeneys — the largest family in the street — nine children and two linnets in cages. The eldest daughter was eleven and the only one of the family who could read. I was feeling wild at the time and fell madly in love with her. She had a bound volume of Grimm's fairy tales and every day we sat on the stairs and read "The Singing Bone" and "The Youth Who Could Not Shiver And Shake". I could do both. And for Maisie Sweeney I could do more. I kissed her cheek. I combed my hair properly and covered it with Bay Rum. And then I tried to seduce her. I asked her if she'd take off all her clothes for a penny. She said she would if I turned my back. I gave her the penny, turned my back, and she screamed for her mother. The mother belted me across the head with the sweeping brush and then reported me to my father. He was upset. But my mother understood perfectly.

"It's natural enough" she said.

"At his age?" cried my father.

"Well, better late than never" said my mother. And that was that.

Two years later I fell in love with Mrs. Cotter. She lived in Mary Street, was forty years old, and the mother of six children. Her husband was a boxer. But my father said he couldn't box eggs, so I ignored him.

When Mrs. Cotter came to visit my mother, which she did as often as she could for a chat and a cigarette, she'd sit on a chair by the fire and cross her legs. Mrs. Cotter was always crossing her legs and I couldn't keep my eyes off them. If I'd told Mr. Goldman about that he'd have said it was nothing more than a mother fixation. It was nothing of the kind. It was lust. And when I told Father Donovan in the Confession Box, he said it was lust and that I ought to be locked up.

I was praying to be locked up. I was down on my knees seven days a week praying to be locked up with Mrs. Cotter. But there

29

was no response. I gave up praying after that. The whole thing is a cod.

8

Jewtown was a long row of red-brick Corporation houses situated close to the gas-works. The houses had lain derelict for years, but were now occupied by the Jews. I asked my father about that and he said that the Jews there had come from Limerick and before that, Romania — or some other such place. They were persecuted there and in Limerick their graveyard had been desecrated by vandals. Now they had settled in Cork.

"The Lord help them" he said.

Jewtown was bleak. But on summer days the women sat on the pavement outside their doors, knitting scarves and pullovers which they later sold around the houses in Evergreen Street and Turner's Cross. The men remained inside. And if you looked through the windows you could see them making leather belts, wallets and handbags — all decorated with twisted pieces of coloured string and beads.

My father said the Jews were poor, but Mr. Egan said they were all rich. My father said he was a thick.

"If they're rich, what the hell are they doing living in Jewtown"? he shouted. "I wouldn't keep a dog in a place like that."

Mr. Egan said that was camouflage. "You couldn't be up to the Jews, they'd have the eyes out of your head if you weren't looking."

My father turned his back on Mr. Egan and refused to talk to him anymore.

"I've been listening to that kind of nonsense from as far back as I can remember. If you're out of work, blame the Jews. If you haven't got enough to eat, blame the Jews. If the water doesn't taste right, the Jews have probably poisoned it. And if it's not the Jews, it's the bloody witches, or both. It's like living in a madhouse."

My mother made tea. My father sat by the fire. My mother handed him a cup.

"I don't know why you take notice of an eegit like that. You know what he's like."

31

"I had to take notice. The boy was listening."

"He's listening now" said my mother. "Why don't you explain?"

My father looked at me. He didn't want to explain. The subject angered him,but he felt he had to say something.

"Have you been to Jewtown?" he asked.

"Yes."

"And you've seen those people down there ?"

"I have."

"Are they any different from us?"

"I don't know."

"Well, I'll tell you. They're not. And some of them are a damned sight worse off. They're the most persecuted people on the face of the Earth, and I have to listen to rubbish like that from Egan! Is it any wonder the country is in the state that it is?"

"Drink your tea" said my mother "before you have a stroke."

My father drank his tea and almost choked swallowing it. "I told you to be careful" my mother scolded — and patted him on the back.

"Mr. Goldman is a Jew" I said. "Why doesn't he live in Jewtown?"

"He used to" my mother answered. "It was his cousin in America who found those rooms in the Marsh. And when he left, Mannie Goldman moved in. I think the cousin still pays the rent."

"He sends him five pounds every Christmas, too."

"The Jews try to help each other" said my mother. "They have to. Nobody else will look after them."

"Did they murder Christ?" I asked.

My parents looked at me. "Divine Jesus!" exclaimed my father. "Who told you that?"

I remembered the night I sat in Mr. Goldman's room when someone threw a brick through the window. I told him what happened. He turned to my mother.

"Did you know about this?"

"No. But it doesn't surprise me."

My father paused. "It doesn't surprise me either" he said. And lapsed into silence. Presently, he spoke.

"I can't read" he said. "And I can't write — but I know how Mannie Goldman must have felt. So would your Grandmother. You should ask her sometime."

"You're his father" said my mother. "You tell him. Trying to get a word out of Lizzie Baron is like pulling teeth."

I sing through my father.

9

When my Grandfather arrived in the city with Lizzie Baron, it was plain to see that she was foreign. Her long black hair. The sun-brown colour of her skin. The dark glow of her eyes. My Grandfather took pride in these things. And when Lizzie lay close by his side. he held her to his heart like a flower.

In the North Side of the city, they managed to find a small house to rent. One room on the ground floor and a loft upstairs where they slept. My father was born there and so was his sister, my Aunt Bridget.

"There was no lavatory" said my father — "just an old shed at the back. But we were happy enough. Bridget and I played in the lanes off Shandon Street and, sometimes, when the circus came to Blackpool, we sat in a tent and watched that."

Those were the good old days. The horses pranced round the sawdust ring and the lions roared at the man with the whip and the monkeys laughed when the penguins danced and the audience gasped when the lady who flew on the flying-trapeze fell down — and was saved — by the man with the net. Those were the good old days.

"That's what they say" my father said. "But I don't remember them like that anymore. I remember one day playing in the street and a boy of about my own age saying to me 'Is your mother a witch?' I didn't know what to make of it at the time, but that was the beginning. My mother was different. She wasn't like other people. And she always wore black. That's a bad sign.

"After a while, other children started asking the same question. They wanted to know whether she could put curses on people and whether she stuffed children into the oven like the witch in "Hansel And Grethel". They followed her in the streets, and when she told them to go away, they laughed because her English was bad and she couldn't pronounce the words properly. She screamed — and that made it even worse because witches always scream and they look at you with a witch's eye and you

33

could catch a disease or maybe go blind or something.

Lizzie Baron is a witch
She casts spells that make you itch
Toads and goblins in her bed
If she reads you, you are dead.

Beat her with a holy stick
Send her down to join Old Nick
If she screeches, don't be slow,
Give the witch another blow.

"And they did. My father complained to the parents and threatened to beat the hell out of the next person who even looked sideways at her. He tried to persude her to ignore the children and go on about her business. But she couldn't. She closed the door, refused to go out, and sat in the corner in silence.

People said she was odd. They stood in pubs and at street corners and said she was strange all right and you could hardly blame the children for being frightened of her. Maybe she did cast spells? There was certainly a curse on this place and some people haven't had a day's work in years. People were dying all over the place with T.B. and God knows what else.And it's all very well saying these things are God's will — but there are other things, you know."

Spells and curses
Hidden rooms
Witches riding on their brooms
Jews and dead men on the prowl
Cross yourself and make them howl.

When you see
The headless coach
Or blood upon the waning moon
Bolt your doors and paint them red
Or in the morning you'll be dead.

"We didn't know then how much worse things could get. When my mother moved from the corner and sat by the fire, children climbed on to the roof and dropped stones down the chimney. Black smoke clouded the room and the hot ash lay scattered across the living-room floor. My father chased the children down the street, but it made no difference. They came back later with more stones.

One day. when my father was out looking for work down the quays and Bridget and I were sitting on the floor playing cards, we thought we could smell smoke coming from the loft. My mother was resting up there, and when we rushed up the stairs we found the curtains were on fire. Someone had thrown a lighted roll of paper through the open window and it was still burning close to the bed.

My mother was fast asleep, but we finally managed to wake her up, and she helped us put the fire out with a bucket of cold water. When I looked out of the window to see if the children were still there, I saw two men standing at the corner. And one of them shouted — "We thought you'd like a bit of heat in there. 'Tis desperate weather!"

After that, my father decided we should move. We went to Kinsale first and stayed in my father's old place overlooking the harbour. But he couldn't settle and, finally, we returned to Cork and found a place on this side of the city.

We had no trouble here and, gradually, your Grandmother started going out again to do her shopping in the English Market. But she hasn't forgotten. I know that, though she seldom speaks now and hasn't been out at all since my father died. But she might talk to you. She likes children. She always has."

Those were the good old days. My father had spoken to me for the first time about his youth. Now he turned away. He reached up to the mantelpiece and removed his tin whistle from it's place behind the clock. He played music. The sun shone through the open window and my mother sang The Culin.

10

I almost drowned once. I fell into the horse's trough below in the South Mall and lay face down in two feet of water. My whole life refused to appear in front of me. It was the beginning of disillusion. My friend, Connors, hauled me out and said I was only trying to draw attention to myself.

Connors was a cynic. He was two years older than me, but we sat in the same class at school because Brother Reynolds said he had only half a brain and was unsuited to a higher grade. Connors was delighted to have only half a brain. It made him feel special.

I was special, too. I had a Grandmother who sat in a corner all day and I had Greek blood in my veins. Connors didn't believe I had Greek blood and wanted to know what colour it was. When I said — pink — he stuck a pin in my arm and waited to see how I would bleed. Sometimes, I hated Connors.

When he was short of money one time, he tried to sell me in an auction. An American liner had arrived in Cork and Connors hung a placard round my neck saying. "This boy is an orphan. Going now to the highest bidder. Any offers?" There were none. If there had been, I might now be President of America and Connors would have made a fortune telling tourists about my humble beginnings.

Connors never had a beginning. He was born in a vacuum. And when his father died from lack of drink, his mother tried to hide him under the floorboards and pretend she was childless. When that failed, she sent him to school and asked Brother Reynolds to keep an eye on him. Brother Reynolds kept both eyes on him and when in doubt locked him in the coal cellar. There were rats in there, but Connors stared them out and emerged hours later blinking but unscathed.

Brother Reynolds gave up. He told Connors to sit in a corner and say nothing. Connors grinned through the gaps in his teeth. He was happy to sit in the corner. He could see the school clock from there and he counted the minutes until it was time for

Brother Reynolds to dismiss us for the day.

Some days, after school, Connors and I went for a walk down the Marina. We climbed on to the quay wall and begged pesetas and drachmas and French francs from the crews of foreign ships. We could see the world from there. The ghosts of corn and timber sails. The flags of nations we would long to visit. The gulls circling over Sweden and Finland, Russia and Scandinavia, and beyond to Egypt where the pyramids stood as a monument to vanity and the death of kings.

We played hide-and-seek beneath the jetties. Dived naked from the slipway steps. Swam in the dull grey waters of the Lee. And then lay on the grass beside Dunlops and Fords to dry out under the last rays of the afternoon sun.

On our way home we paused to see the Innisfallen leave its berth. We saw it turn and move out, drift slowly past Blackrock Castle and head towards the Atlantic. We saw it enter the night, its decks crowded with emigrants from Cork — most of whom were destined never to return.

Connors often talked about emigrating from Cork. He'd seen Ronald Coleman in "Under Two Flags" at the Savoy cinema and was determined to join the French Foreign Legion. He changed his mind later when he saw Gary Cooper in "Lives Of A Bengal Lancer". That made him want to join the British Army and defend the Empire on the North West Frontier of India.

His mother encouraged him. She wanted him to go to Australia or Burma, or Mongolia or the Gobi Desert or anywhere as long as he was out of the house. Mrs. Connors wasn't pleased with her son. And her son wasn't too keen on her either. He was convinced she was trying to starve him to death.

"The food she gives me is rotten. I think she wants to be a nun."

Mrs. Connors did want to be a nun. The convent beckoned her, but she was lumbered with her son. If she could have sent him into outer space she would have done so gladly. She prayed for the Martians to come. She went down on her knees and offered up The Rosary for a merciful release. She closed her eyes, but when she opened them again he was still standing there, staring her in the face.

"Does she have holy pictures in the house?"

"All over the shagging place" said Connors.

I had never been inside Connors's house. His mother wouldn't permit it. She was against visitors unless they were ordained priests or fully paid up members of the The Legion Of Mary. She had the house consecrated to the Sacred Heart and a statue of Saint Anthony guarding the front door. There was no way past him.

"It's a wonder she lets me in" said Connors. "But she only does that to torment me."

Mrs. Connors was always tormenting him. On weekdays, she made him his breakfast of tea and bread and dripping but only after she'd dragged him to early Mass in the South Chapel in Dunbar street. In the evenings, she made him a pot of soup, but Connors said you wouldn't know what she'd put into it and he was afraid to look.

Sunday, however, was her best day. She locked the larder door then and spent the whole day fasting. She expected Connors to do the same, but he came round to our place and ate us all out of house and home. My mother thought Mrs. Connors was demented — and she had grave doubts about her son. But she fed him when she could.

The house they lived in was small and dark and it stood close to the South Presentation Convent in Abbey Street. Mrs. Connors could see the nuns from there and the light burning in the convent chapel.

"She says the light is the eye of God and if it goes out she'll die. I told her I'd blow it out meself if she didn't stop annoying me, but she takes no notice."

Connors hated the light. It shone through the window at night and he couldn't get to sleep. He tried counting sheep, and when that failed, he hid under the bed. But the light followed him, like a spectre cast from the runes, and there was no escape.

When his father was alive the window had been blocked up. When he died, Mrs. Connors had it opened again.

"It's like living near a lighthouse now" said Connors "I've shifted the bed three times, but I'm still blinded".

"Didn't your father believe in God?"

"He did not! The only thing he believed in was land reform and capital punishment for people with religion. I didn't know what he was talking about at the time. 'Tis only dawning on me now. That's why she wants rid of me."

"Are you going to run away?"

39

"I will one day. But I'd hate to leave the Da. He's buried in Saint Finbarr's now and I go and talk to him sometimes. You'd think she'd do the same — but she never goes near the place. She says my father is in Hell and there's nothing she can do about that."

Connors survived his mother and when she died he buried her with the statue of Saint Anthony planted firmly in her lap. Later, he had the window boarded up and slept blissfully in a darkened room.

11

The quays were black. My father was unemployed and the consensus of opinion was that I should look for a job after school. With Mr. Goldman's help I applied for a job as a messenger-boy and was rewarded with an interview with a Mr. Thomas A. Grogan.

Mr. Grogan was a butcher. who also passed himself off as a grocer, and he required a strong lad who could climb mountains with a basket-load of groceries and the slaughtered remains of cattle and sheep. He was offering a salary of seven shillings and sixpence per week and the applicant was required to ride a bike. I could ride a bike — provided the wind was westerly. I omitted to mention this to Mr. Grogan.

"You don't look very strong" he piqued.

"I'm as strong as a horse" I said.

"I'm not looking for a horse" said Mr. Grogan. "Can you ride a bike?"

I looked at the bike. It was large, black, and clearly designed to withstand the abuses of legions of messenger boys. Mr. Grogan waited.

"Well?"

"Tis no trouble, Mr. Grogan."

"We'll see."

He laid his hand on my head and steered me towards the bike. "I've had it specially made" he said.

And I could see that. The handlebars were solid. The wheels were made of cast iron and the carrier-basket, welded to the frame in front, was guaranteed by its makers to bear the maximum of weight with the minimum of strain to the bike — if not to the messenger-boy.

"I've had messenger-boys before" Mr Grogan groaned. "They were not up to it."

"Try me, Mr. Grogan."

"Don't rush me. I'm thinking." Mr. Grogan thought. His gaze wandered from the toes of my feet to the crown of my head. He was not impressed.

41

"How old are you ?"

"Ten."

He shook his head. He walked round me. He examined my back, pressed down on my shoulders, looked at my hands and then opened my mouth.

"If you were a horse, I wouldn't give twopence for you."

I straightened myself up. I tried to look like the wrestler, Dano Mahoney. I said I was a personal friend of Jack Doyle, the boxer. I said that his wife, Movita, had recommended me. Mr. Grogan shook his head again — and he went on shaking it until I thought it would fall off.

Presently, he said — "I must be mad in the head, but you're falling apart and my heart goes out to you. You can start on Monday."

"Thanks, Mr. Grogan."

"And remember this — I pay seven shillings and sixpence a week and I expect value for that."

"Yes, Mr. Grogan."

I backed away. I was now an employee. I kept my head low.

On Monday afternoon, I arrived at Mr. Grogan's shop. He was standing at the door, the bike beside him, and the carrier basket was loaded with the day's deliveries. He handed me a list of names and addresses.

"You'll find most of those are for Saint Lukes and Montonette. The rest are for the Good Shepherd's Convent. I'll expect you back at five. Understood?"

"Yes, Mr. Grogan."

He turned his back and disappeared into the shop.

I stared at the bike. It was overloaded and when I touched it, the saddle rose in the air and the rear wheel followed it. I pressed it down with my hands and managed to climb onto the saddle. But when I tried to reach the pedals, I found that my legs were too short. There was no way I could ride it.

I climbed down, pressed hard on the saddle with one hand and wheeled the bike along Prince's Street towards Patrick Street. By the time, I reached Patrick's Bridge I was exhausted.

I paused for a moment to catch my breath — and then I saw my friend Connors. He was leaning against the parapet of the bridge and he was smirking.

"Oh ! he says. Working, are we ?"

I hate people who smirk and there were times when I could

have spat poisoned darts at Connors — but I restrained myself.

"You'll never make it", he said. "By the time you reach McCurtain Street you'll be dead."

"You could at least give me a hand!"

"Sorry, old stock, but I'm not feeling too well. That's why I've been off school for a week."

"You don't look sick."

"I know. It's one of those foreign diseases. Doesn't show on the face. Who are you working for?"

"Grogans."

"Holy Jasus!" exclaimed Connors. "Don't you know about him? He's a monster. Nosey Donaghue worked for him last year and he's crippled now."

"Who says?"

"I do. I went to visit him in the Union a couple of days ago and he can't even get out of bed!"

My heart blenched. There was a stabbing pain in my right leg. I felt distinctly unwell.

I knew Nosey. He was strong. He had muscles coming out of his ears. He could walk on broken glass. I didn't know he'd worked in Grogans.

"Not any more he doesn't" said Connors. "He'll be on crutches for life. If I was you I'd go home. Push that bike into the river and run for it."

"I can't. I need the job."

"Connors smirked again and gave a consumptive cough for the poor of Cork.

"Oh well", he spluttered. "I'll see you in the Union.

"Are you not going to give me a push?"

Connors paused. "I'll tell you what I'd do" he said. "You collect the bike every day from Grogans. Wheel it round as far as Patrick Street and I'll wait for you there. I'll give you a hand as far as Saint Lukes."

"And then what?"

"After that, you make the deliveries. And when you've finished you can sit in the basket and I'll ride the bicycle down the hill."

"How much?"

"A shilling a week from your wages. It's for nothing! I'm only doing it as a favour."

I agreed under pressure. My wages had been reduced by a

shilling, but it was worth it to keep the job. And Connors kept his word.

Every day, he helped me push the bike up as far as Saint Lukes and when I'd completed my deliveries I sat in the carrier-basket and Connors free-wheeled the bicycle down the hill. I might have known it couldn't last.

One day, the brakes gave out. The bicycle ran out of control and we crashed into the front door of the Coliseum cinema at the bottom of the hill. I sprained an arm and Connors spent six weeks in the South Infirmary with a broken collarbone.

"I always knew working was a mug's game" he said. "Next time, get someone else!"

I didn't need someone else. When Mr. Grogan saw the wreckage of the bike and my sprained arm, his heart went out to me again. He said I could work in the slaughter-house for a while and help the men to keep the floors clean. As an afterthought he announced that he would deduct part of my wages every week to cover the cost of repairing the bike.

12

I had never been inside a slaughter-house.

The pens were filled with the sounds of death. The animals jostled and strained against the wooden fence and against each other. They sweated and steamed and their breath clouded the air above them.

A man appeared. He wore a black leather apron over his corduroy trousers and he wore wooden clogs. His footsteps echoed across the yard as he moved towards the enclosure.

The bull saw him coming. He pawed the ground and snorted, but the man ignored him. The bull snorted again, the white froth issuing from its mouth and hanging in trails from his lower lip. The man stared at him for a moment and then prodded him with a steel rod. The bull lowered its head, as if to charge, but there was no room.

The man circled the pen and approached him from the rear. He prodded the bull again, forcing him in the direction of a narrow gang-plank leading to the slaughter-house. When the bull reached the gang-plank he stumbled, but the man continued to prod until the bull rose to its feet and stumbled again as he headed towards the slaughter-house door. Here, he stopped. He could go no further. The door was closed.

The bull tried to move back, but a steel gate had fallen behind him and he was trapped. He kicked at the gate with his hind legs. He rammed his head against the door of the slaughter-house, and he used all his strength in a vain attempt to climb over the side of the gang-plank. But he was locked in, without room to manoeuvre, and in the end he fell exhausted before the door.

The man moved off and returned a moment later carrying a long rope over his shoulders. He tied one end of the rope around the bull's neck and pushed the other end through a gap under the slaughter-house door. He entered the slaughter-house through a side entrance and pulled the rope through.

The slaughter-house was cold. The walls were painted white

and an iron ring lay embedded in the centre of the concrete floor. The man drew the rope through the ring and hitched the end to a stout beam directly above his head. He lit a cigarette and waited for the slaughterman to arrive.

Mr. Cunningham was tall. He'd been a slaughterman for twenty-five years and he was proud of his profession. He wore white overalls. He kept his fingernails clean and he carried a sledgehammer in his hand — the steel head pointed at one end. He nodded to the man. The man dropped his cigarette on the ground and stamped it out with his foot. Mr. Cunningham looked at him with disapproval. He was against smoking in the slaughter-house.It was unhygienic.

When the slaughter-house door was opened, the bull rose to his feet and stared into the opening before him. He sniffed the air and he could smell the blood. He drew back, but the men pulled hard on the rope and dragged him down towards the iron ring embedded in the floor.

The bull roared. He twisted and turned and tried desperately to extricate himself from the choking rope, but the rope held him and the more he struggled the tighter it became.

He fell to the floor, his forelegs buckling under him, but the men continued to draw on the rope until the bull's head touched the iron ring and his hind legs rose in the air, kicking wildly upon an empty space.

When they had tied the rope securely to the beam above them, Mr. Cunningham approached the bull. He picked up the sledgehammer from the ground beside him and struck the bull on the forehead with the pointed end. The bull's body convulsed with shock and Mr. Cunningham struck him again on the same spot until a hole appeared and the blood gushed forth in a fountain of red.

Mr. Cunningham lowered the sledgehammer. He wiped his hands with a clean white cloth.He inserted a hooked wire into the hole he had just created in the bull's forehead and then, very gently, he extracted the brain.

I stood at the slaughter-house door and vomited.

13

Every Sunday after Mass, the neighbours gathered in our tenement flat to sing and tell stories. My father played music and, sometimes, recited poetry he'd made up in his head. My father would never admit to having made up these poems. He said they were the work of great men long gone and now sadly neglected. My mother said he was the biggest liar in Cork — and he was. But he was also a poet. A poet is a man who tell lies, but in short lines and with style. My father had style.

Paddy Tom Kilroy also had style. He lived over in Frenches Quay and everyone called him The Captain because he wore a sailor's cap and had never been to sea. He owned a small fishing-boat, too. It was willed to him by his father and was moored near the South Gate Bridge, but Paddy had never set foot on it. He said the weather was too bad.

The weather had started to go bad fifteen years ago when Paddy's father had died and left him the boat. It was still bad and there was no sign of an improvement.

Paddy leaned over the parapet of the South Gate Bridge and stared at the boat. The timbers were rotting. The seagulls were nesting on the deck and the barnacles were choking the hull to death.

Paddy looked at the sky. If only the weather would improve — but he knew it wouldn't. He'd read in the newspaper that morning that there was a storm brewing over Cork. He buttoned his coat. The weather was killing him. He could feel it in his bones.

One Sunday, Paddy arrived at our flat in Margaret Street and said he'd changed into a seagull. He didn't look like a seagull, and he still wore his sailor's cap, but my father invited him in and asked him if he'd seen a doctor? Paddy shook his head. There was no point. Doctors knew nothing about seagulls and, besides, he was happy enough the way he was. Come to think of it — he'd always wanted to be a seagull, but the boat got in his way.

My father thought he'd gone raving mad, but my mother was

47

more sympathetic. She offered him fish. Paddy ate the fish and said he'd never tasted anything sweeter in his life. On his way out, he thanked my mother and said he'd remember her in his will. My father almost choked. He hated fish and he was convinced that Paddy would be in the madhouse within the week.

A few days later, Paddy returned to the house. My mother found him sitting on the stairs and there were tears in his eyes. He said the police were after him, and when my mother asked him what crime he'd committed, he said he hadn't committed a crime. All he'd done was to fly in and out of the South Chapel during Mass and screech — "More Fish"!

The congregation was terrified and the Parish Priest had a heart attack — but whose fault was that? A seagull was a perfectly harmless bird and all the congregation had to do was to say "Sorry, Paddy, we've run out of fish" and Paddy would have been satisfied and gone elsewhere.

When the police arrived, Paddy was wheeled off to the Bridewell and he spent a week in there flapping his wings about and claiming that under International Law it was illegal to imprison a seagull.

The guards at the Bridewell knew nothing about International Law, but they insisted that under Irish Law the police could arrest anyone for anything — even of he were a seagull.

Paddy applied for bail, and my mother had to pawn my father's best suit in order to raise the money to have Paddy released.

My father was a tolerant man, but when his best suit had to be pawned to have a seagull released from jail, things were getting out of hand altogether. He had nothing against seagulls — provided they let their droppings fall on someone else — but this particular seagull was getting on his nerves. He wanted his suit back — and he said so without music.

My mother laughed. She knew that Paddy was a genius, and if he felt he was a seagull, then that's what he was. After all, there were worse things he could be -like a policeman or a Blueshirt. My father didn't agree at all and was now beginning to worry about my mother. Any minute now and she'd be sprouting wings.

She didn't. She pulled her black shawl tightly around her

shoulders and went to the courthouse the following morning to hear Paddy being charged with a breach of the peace. He pleaded "Not Guilty" and when the magistrate asked him for his full name he replied :

"Seagulls don't have full names. They're just called — Seagulls."

The magistrate nodded his head. He understood perfectly. Paddy was a poet. He dismissed the case and Paddy winged it from the court a free bird.

He was missing for months. My mother searched around his usual haunts, but there was no trace of him. Paddy had disappeared.

Then, one day, while she was sitting in a pub in Sullivan's Quay, having her usual bottle of stout, the door opened and Paddy walked in. She offered him a drink. Paddy accepted and sat beside her in the snug.

"You've been away?" she said.

"I have" Paddy declared. "Do you notice anything different about me?"

My mother wasn't sure. Paddy shook his head. He was no longer a seagull.

"That's a sad day for Cork, Paddy."

"It's a sad day for me too, Maam. But the fates were against it."

He finished his drink and turned towards the door.

"By the way he said — "I've willed you the boat. Maybe your son will find a use for it."

"I'm sure he will" said my mother. "But you'll be with us for a long time yet, Paddy."

Paddy shrugged his shoulders. "I'll be going now" he said. "Thanks for the drink."

"Are you going far?"

"I'm going for a walk on the water" Paddy replied. "God knows when I'll be back."

The door closed behind him and a week later Paddy's body was found floating on the water close to Blackrock Castle. My mother wept — and the seagulls carried Paddy home.

14

My mother believed in poets. She said they were not born but invented by God to celebrate his angels. My father believed in my mother, but thought poets should be heard and not seen. The anonymous poem was the real poem. It belonged to everyone and not just to the messenger who happened to deliver a first copy. My father could be complicated at times. It was hard to know what he was talking about. My mother said it was best not to ask. It only made confusion worse confounded.

When he was a young man — and long before he'd met my mother — my father joined the British Army and served with the Royal Munster Fusiliers in India. You could tell he'd been to India because when he was drunk he recited "Gunga Din" and when he was sad he talked about the foothills and the Ganges and the nabobs and the moguls who were presented with their weight in diamonds every time they had a birthday.

My father never celebrated his birthday — and he hated uniforms. And when I asked him why he had joined the British Army he said he had no idea. He just happened to be passing by the Recruiting Office one day and he heard a voice crying — "I Want You!" When he turned around, he saw General Haig standing there and he hadn't the heart to refuse him.

The General was polite enough. He wanted to know how old my father was and when my father said he couldn't remember, the General had him medically examined. The doctor looked through one ear and couldn't see out through the other — and my father was in. The General promised to meet him in France, but my father boarded the wrong boat at Southampton and the next thing he knew he was in Calcutta singing "God Save The King" whom he'd never met.

When he tried to explain all this to my mother one day she developed a migraine headache from which she never fully recovered.

My father liked India. He felt it was his spiritual home and he was happy to sit by the Ganges all day contemplating the

Universe. The army, however, had other ideas. They taught him how to box.

He ran five miles under the blazing sun every day and then he worked-out in the gym. He developed muscles in places he never knew existed. He skipped and he danced. He rubbed salt on his face and steeped his hands in vinegar and brine. He punched leather until the gloves split, exposing the protective bandages underneath. And then he ran another five miles until the heat drained him of everything but fists and hard driving bone.

The army were proud of my father. They said he was a natural in the ring. They promoted him to Corporal and entered him in competitions all over India. He stood against the best that the continent could provide and in three years he had fought his way up to become Amateur Boxing Champion of the British Army in India. And then he quit.

He gave no reason. He offered no explanation. He simply hung up his gloves and walked away.

When my father left the army and returned to Cork, he still maintained an interest in boxing, but he refused to enter the ring and he never talked about his own experiences as a boxer. Instead he told stories about the great boxers of the past -from John L. Sullivan and Jim Corbett — Jack Dempsey and Gene Tunney — Max Bear and Tony Galento — James Braddock — and the then current champion — Joe Louis. He talked about Len Harvey, who was light on his feet and should have been a ballet dancer, and Jack Doyle who could sing but wasn't hungry enough to be a great champion.

He knew about them all and could list their achievements and their failures. And he knew how they felt when the bell sounded for the first round and how they felt when the final bell heralded victory or defeat. He had tasted both and had not been counted out.

He said boxing was a poem. He said Jim Corbett created images with his feet and Joe Louis painted pictures with his fists. My mother couldn't understand a word of it and said the British had a lot to answer for. She could be complicated too and had her own way of looking at things.

She blest the Irish Rebellion of Nineteen Sixteen and said that Connolly and Pearse were two of the greatest Irishmen who ever lived. My father thought Pearse was a lunatic and that Connolly was led astray by a lot of codology.

My mother supported the Russian Revolution of Nineteen Seventeen. My father said she'd think differently when the Communists invaded Cork.

My mother sided with the Diehards during the Irish Civil War and said that Michael Collins should have been shot dead the moment he returned from London having signed the Anglo Irish Treaty. My father thought it was better to settle for half a loaf than none at all.

My mother mentioned McSweeney who died on hunger strike in Brixton Prison. My father remembered the funeral.

My mother thought we should burn everything in Ireland except British coal. My father said he would burn anything if it kept the house warm.

My mother said he should never have joined the British Army. My father said he loved India.

My mother said he ought to be ashamed of himself. My father said he was not.

She wrote —" La Pasionaria is the noblest woman on Earth". My father couldn't read and had never heard of Dolores Ibarruri.

My father and my mother loved each other and they lived happily together for a time.

53

15

Lefty Thompson was my father's friend and though he too had joined the British Army during the Great War, my mother admired him because he was now on the side of the Spanish Republicans and stood with Mr. Goldman at the corner of Washington Street to protest against the Fascists. My father did not protest against the Fascists, but he wouldn't support them either. He said Lefty was his friend — and that was enough. Lefty understood. My mother did not. She said there were times when friendship wasn't enough.

She wanted him to stand beside Lefty and Mr. Goldman and protest in a loud voice. She wanted him to paint slogans on the walls and declare who he was and what he stood for — but my father said no. He was not that kind of man. He could play the tin whistle. He would not deny his friends and he would keep open house for all those who could sing or play music, or appreciate a good story or a poem. That's who he was. That's what he stood for. That was my father.

Lefty was different. He could not play the tin whistle, but he could tolerate a good story and he could sing when his throat was oiled with a sufficient quantity of liquor. And he was taller than my father.

He stood six feet and six inches in height and the muscles on his arms stood out like the tow ropes on a battleship. My father said he could have been one of the great boxers of the age — if only he had two legs.

Lefty did have two legs at one time, but he lost one of them during the Great War because he had no luck and boarded the right boat for France at Southampton, when he should have boarded the wrong one, like my father, and ended up in India.

Lefty would have enjoyed India. The French irritated him. And when he arrived in France and was met by General Haig — the General irritated him by trying to kiss him on both cheeks and saying "You're just in time for the Big Push".

Lefty had heard about the Big Push and he knew that the General had already lost about forty thousand men in a previous Big Push and the only thing he'd gained was fifty yards of mud flats. Lefty wasn't too pleased about that and thought the General was an idiot. He wanted to go home.But the General wasn't sending people home that day. He was sending them all to the Front to take part in the Big Push.

The General was beset with the Big Push — "Once more. Thompson, and we'll all be home by Christmas". But on Christmas Day, Lefty was still sitting in the trenches with his feet in three feet of muddy water while the General was playing leap-frog with his subordinates in the Officer's Mess.

When the General had finished playing leap-frog he ordered everyone "Over The Top!" and Lefty was so happy to get out of the trenches that he was first over — and the only thing he remembered after that was waking up in hospital and wondering where the rest of him had gone.

The Surgeon didn't know. Lefty asked him twice — but the Surgeon had amputated so many legs recently that he could no longer tell one from another and had no idea where he'd thrown the ones he'd cut off.

"It was the right one" said Lefty.

"It's always the right one!" exclaimed the Surgeon. "I never amputate anything else. Was there a scar on it?"

"There was" replied Lefty. "I fell off me roller skates when I was five."

"It could be anywhere" the Surgeon declared. "Better ask General Haig."

But when Lefty asked the General where his right leg had gone — the General didn't know either.

"Are you sure you had two when you went over the top?" he asked Lefty.

"Oh yes, Sir. I remember distinctly. Two legs. A right and a left."

"Most extraordinary. Well, Thompson keep your pecker up. I'll enquire about the missing leg. In the meantime, congratulations. We gained ten yards yesterday. Unfortunately, we lost them again this morning — but we'll keep trying, eh!"

"Yes, Sir. May I ask about the number of casualties?"

"Of course. Good luck, Thompson. Jolly good luck."

And that was the last that Lefty saw of General Haig.

Two months later, Lefty was discharged from the army and everyone called him Hoppy though he preferred to called

56

"Lefty". He received a pension of eleven shillings a week and the British Legion provided him with a bread-voucher enabling him to obtain a free loaf every Friday at the local bakery.

General Haig did slightly better. He was made an Earl and the Government awarded him a grant of One Hundred Thousand Pounds to help him cover his household expenses. When he vacated the house in 1928 and moved into the real No Man's Land, he was exhausted but fulfilled.

Lefty lived longer. He made himself a boxcar out of two planks of wood and four pram wheels and he propelled himself around the city like a child practising for the Grand Prix. He called himself The Socialist and was arrested for disorderly behaviour in Patrick Street when he made a speech advocating free love and the equal distribution of wealth. My father was all in favour of the latter, but the notion of free love gave him arthritis. My mother was more flexible — *Que Sera Sera...*

During the last days of his life, Lefty tried to make a living selling postcards of Revolutionary Heroes at two for a penny in the Coal Quay Market. He was not successful. And when he died he left his body to science with instructions that when they had finished with the remains they were to cast them into the nearest dustbin. He added a postscript to that :

"Sorry about the missing leg, lads. But see what you can do with the remaining one."

He was buried at night, near the banks of the Lee, in a dustbin filled with red carnations.

16

Monday was murder-day. The school-room clock struck high noon and Brother Reynolds stood with his back to the wall and sniffed the air. He said he could smell treason. His nose twitched. His hands shook and his gaze wandered from desk to desk and from boy to boy. He studied our faces. He searched behind our eyes for traces of shame and guilt — and when he found them he smiled and ordered the unlucky ones to come forth. My friend Connors and I came forth. We admitted our guilt. We confessed our shame. We had not been to ten o'clock mass the previous Sunday and we knew we were damned.

Brother Reynolds said we were damned. He said that on the final Day of Judgement we would stand before the Lord God of Hosts and He would say unto us – "Woe be to those who did not attend ten o'clock mass on Sunday. Depart from me, ye cursed, into the everlasting flames of Hell which was prepared for the Devil and his angels."

Connors and I departed. We sank into Hell. The Devil was pushing red hot pokers into our ears and Brother Reynolds was beating us across the palms of the hands with a pure ash cane. Six slaps each and an extra one for Sunday because that was a holy day.

My friend Connors thought holy days were a cod and said his mother had invented them for the sole purpose of torturing his father. When he told Brother Reynolds that, Brother Reynolds beat him again until the cane split wide open — and then he told him to kneel on the floor and ask God for forgiveness. My friend Connors did kneel on the floor and he prayed hard.But he prayed he'd grow up to be a millionaire so that he could afford to hire a hit-man and have his mother assassinated.

I prayed for Brother Reynolds. I prayed that his eyes would fall out and drop on the floor and we could all play football. But I forgot I'd given up praying and when there was no response I sank deeper into Hell.

Brother Reynolds explained about Hell. He said he'd seen it

in a dream and it had seven levels and the deepest level was reserved for boys who had bad thoughts and never went to ten o'clock mass on Sunday. I had bad thoughts. I was in love with Mickey Rooney and I wanted to sleep with Ann Sheridan. Mr. Goldman said I was confused.

Brother Reynolds was never confused. He had three ash canes and he used them with zeal on all those who had not been to ten o'clock mass. And when those canes were broken on the hands of children who were forever damned he'd send me down to the Institute of the Blind to collect more canes. I wondered about the blind. Did they know that they were making canes to beat people to death who could see? Brother Reynolds would know. Brother Reynolds knew everything.

He knew that I hadn't been to ten o'clock mass on the previous Sunday because I sold newspapers in the street on Saturday nights and then went to the late-night cinema to see Ken Maynard riding a white horse. He knew that I slept late on Sundays and was too tired to get out of bed. He knew that I had a mania for the cinema and was crippled trying to walk like James Cagney. And he knew that if I had enough money I would build a cinema of my own and let nobody in but Connors and myself.

Brother Reynolds didn't approve of the cinema. He never sold newspapers in the street and he never tried to walk like James Cagney. He would not be damned. He stayed up all night waiting for ten o'clock mass on Sunday morning.

Brother Leary, on the other hand, did not concern himself with ten o'clock mass. At another time, upon another level in Hell, he sat on a chair and struggled to teach us that two and two did not make five. He tried hard, but no one was interested and the knowledge burned him. So he turned to the bottle — and every day when he entered the classroom he carried a small flask of whiskey in his back pocket. That was his comfort and when he had drained the flask he sucked the neck of it dry and cried "Mama!" to the world and to all who could hear him. Brother Reynolds heard him and said he was a drunk, but the children were used to drunks and simply ignored him until he fell on the floor — and then they carried him to his desk where he slept peacefully with his head resting on piles of discarded jotters and sheets of pink blotting-paper.

You could feel sorry for Brother Leary. He was a small twisted

60

little man with a wingy expression and a drooping moustache. He had hairs in his ears and when he spoke his teeth rattled like chaneys in a box. He said his life was sore and you wondered what he meant, but he knew you didn't care and that knowledge too filled him with despair.

Sometimes, Brother Leary tried to hide his drinking habits. He hid the flask behind the blackboard — covered the board with numbers and equations and then asked us to copy them all down in our jotters. When he was satisfied that we were all duly ensconced he'd slip behind the blackboard and help himself to a drink.

He didn't know about children and had forgotten how well they can see through blackboards and chalk. We could smell the whiskey. We could taste his sense of disillusion. He counted out the number of his days and found them all wanting.

When Brother Leary was young, his parents said he was born to be a priest. You could tell by the way he looked at you — and he had halo round his head. But Brother Leary had no intention of becoming a priest. He was more interested in politics and in the War of Independence that was then raging across the country. He joined the IRA and fought against the British Army in the hills around Cork. He organised ambushes and laid land mines on the roads. He blew up bridges and was reputed to have personally executed two Black And Tans who were involved in the attempted burning of Cork in December 1920. The British put a price on his head, but he fled to America where he remained until the war was over. Then he returned to Ireland and found that those he had fought beside for so long were now killing each other in a murderous Civil War that was to last for years.

Brother Leary was sick. He saw his past inglorious and the present a bogland of lost hopes and wasted aspirations. He sought refuge in the church and became a Brother In Christ, only to find that his remaining days would be spent teaching mathematics to children who were born to emigrate from the country he had fought to set free.

When Brother Leary drank, it was to relieve the pain and to blot out the agonies of disillusion. But the pain remained and the disillusion remained until a car he was driving crashed into a wall and he died drunk at the wheel.

17

If there was a University in Cork in my youth, I was not aware of it. The cinema was my university and Mr. Goldman said it was a great art — but only as long as the actors remained silent. The moment Al Jolson opened his big mouth in The Jazz Singer everything fell apart. Maybe Mr. Goldman was right, but I was made for the talkies.

Any pocket-money I had I spent at the local cinema. And when I hadn't any pocket-money I stood outside the Savoy and The Pavilion and gazed in wonder at portraits of the Hollywood stars. W.S. Hart riding the back lot range. William Boyd before he became Hopalong Cassidy. Paulette Godard bathing in ass's milk. Edward G. Robinson discovering a cure for the unmentionable. James Cagney in "Public Enemy". Mickey Rooney staging a Broadway musical in his back garden. And most of all and most again — Ann Sheridan. I gazed on her with trembling heart and (I can reveal it now) we were married secretly in Cork by Pat O'Brien who played the priest.

Is it any wonder then that when I saw an advertisement in *The Evening Echo* for a part-time Assistant Projectionist at our local flea pit I applied at once? You can be sure I did. I was tailor made for the job and the owner knew it. His name was Quasimodo.

He was called Quasimodo because he announced the beginning of each programme by charging through the cinema with a bell in each hand shouting "Sanctuary! Sanctuary! We'll begin in a minute." He was also in love with Lon Chaney and, in later years, developed a passion for Charles Laughton. I understood how he felt, but all I wanted to do was to make love to Ann Sheridan and my loins ached from yearning.

Quasimodo had no interest in Ann Sheridan. If he'd had his way he would have shown "The Hunchback Of Notre Dame" twice a day and three times on Sundays. He would have sat in the cinema alone and he would have died for Lon Chaney.

When I arrived for interview on the first day, Quasimodo asked me to spell Lon Chaney's name. I spelt it correctly and was hired on the spot. Quasimodo then explained the duties of an Assistant Projectionist — Evenings Only — No alcholic beverages allowed in the Projection Room :

"An Assistant Projectionist he declared is a man — or in your case, a boy — who sorts out the reels of film delivered to the cinema twice weekly by the renters of said film. He examines the reels. Numbers them in the correct order and then helps the Chief Projectionist to insert them into the projector. A very simple procedure, really. Anyone could do it."

"And what does the Chief Projectionist do?" I asked.

"Very little," replied Quasimodo.

"Could I speak to him?"

"Not at the moment."

"You mean he's not here?"

"He'll be back next week."

Quasimodo then took me by the hand and led me towards the Projection Box. He pointed out the two giant projectors bolted to the floor.

"There are one or two little things I forgot to mention" he said.

"Like what?"

"Well, to begin with, dear boy, all these films are highly inflammable. That means that they are quite likely to burst into flames at the slightest rise in temperature. And, secondly, each projector is equipped with two blue sticks of charcoal. These have to be lit and held closely together during the running of the film. If you allow them to drift apart, the screen will turn blue. If you push them too close together, the projector will overheat and the whole thing will explode. Are you with me so far?"

"I think so."

"Then there's the matter of the reels. Sometimes, they arrive broken. And sometimes the actual film may be damaged. You'll have to look out for that."

"Is it dangerous?"

"Not necessarily. The important thing is to be careful. If you insert a broken reel into the projector the film will probably come to a grinding halt and the audience will throw missiles at the screen. They have, after all, paid fourpence."

"And the damaged film?"

"Ah — that's tricky. A damaged film may get caught up in the sprockets of the projector. In which case, the remainder of the film will spill out on to the floor and catch fire. As I say — the important thing is to be careful."

I promised to be careful and, once again, asked him when the Chief Projectionist was due back.

"Monday or Tuesday" replied Quasimodo. "The doctors have assured me that it shouldn't take longer than a week. In the meantime, do you think you could manage by yourself?"

I said I'd try. I pinned a photograph of Ann Sheridan to the wall above the projectors and pleaded with her for guidance. She did not let me down. Her eyes protected me. Her smile filled me with confidence. I approached the projectors.

"Now, the first thing to remember" said Ann "is that there are two projectors and each reel of film lasts about twenty minutes. You insert Reel One into the first projector and Reel Two into the second projector — making sure beforehand that you have made a number of scratches near the end of each reel so that you'll know when it's about to end. I would suggest that you make these scratches on the top right hand corner of the film."

"Yes, Ann."

"You then tie a piece of string to the shutter of the first projector and link it to the shutter on the second projector — and keep it tight. Then push the starter coil and away you go."

"God bless you, Ann."

"I'm sure He will. Now, during the running of the film it is essential to keep one eye on the screen and the other eye on the two burning sticks of charcoal. When you see the scratches appearing on the top right hand corner of the screen — you pull the piece of string — shutting off the first projector and starting up number two. If you do this quickly enough you will avoid the words End Of Part One appearing on the screen and you will achieve a fine sense of continuity."

"Beautiful."

"Finally — remove Reel One from the first projector and insert Reel Three. And so on until you reach Reel Eight. By that time the film should be completed and you can wrap up and go home".

"With you, Ann?"

Natch, Sweetheart. And if an accident occurs — don't worry. I will always visit you in hospital.

But there was no need for her to visit me in hospital. The

Chief Projectionist failed to return and I survived as an Assistant Projectionist until the cinema was closed because it was considered a potential fire hazard. Quasimodo wept.

He sat in the stalls on that final day and saw "The Hunchback of Notre Dame" for the last time in his own cinema. "Sanctuary! Sanctuary!" he cried as I closed the doors and carried the photograph of Ann Sheridan with me into the light.

Where is she now? Where have they gone — the snows of yesteryear? Come home. Come home. All is forgiven. Come home...

18

I suppose, in some ways, you could say that my Aunt Bridget was a little mad. Certainly, many people thought so. She wore a flaming red blouse, a billowing black skirt, a pair of men's boots — and she told stories to children. It was night when I met her.

I was sitting on the pavement outside Miss Mac's sweet shop in Mary Street when she appeared round the corner carrying all her worldly possessions in a paper bag. She asked who I was. And when I told her she said "I'm your Aunt Bridget".

"The mad one?"

"That's what they say. Is your father at home?"

"No. They're all out."

"I'll sit with you then till they come back."

She sat beside me on the pavement and opened her bag. She removed a handful of sweets and offered me one.

"I'm not supposed to take sweets from strangers."

"I'm not a stranger" she said. "I'm your Aunt."

"My father said you were mad. You ran away from home and joined the gipsies. You were all right before that."

"Was I?"

"I don't know. They don't talk about you now. Have you come home?"

"I think so."

"I'll take the sweet so. You can live with us." And so she did — until she found her own house at the bottom of Evergreen Street.

In her youth, my father said, Aunt Bridget was known as a very respectable girl. She went to Mass regularly, was educated in a convent and learned to bow her head demurely in the presence of the opposite sex. She spoke, but only when she was asked, and never interrupted when her elders and betters were engaged in serious conversation.

When she reached the age of forty, however, she took what my father described as a desperate turn for the worst. No one knows how it happened but, one day, she looked at herself in the mirror and said — no. And the following day she changed her

67

clothes, bought herself a pair of men's boots, and announced that from now on she was going to wander the roads of Ireland and tell stories to children. She kept her word — and the stories she told were magic.

There was the joyous story of a young girl who found a butterfly who had lost its colours. The girl painted new colours on the butterfly and the butterfly flew away to create a rainbow over the city. And listening to my Aunt I could see that rainbow. It arced its way through the Autumn skies and I could see its reflection in my Aunt's eyes.

Then there was the story of the young boy who climbed the highest mountain in the world and when he reached the peak he found the portrait of a woman etched deep in the rock. And the strange thing about that story was that no one had climbed that mountain before — or so it was said.

Oh, my Aunt could tell a story all right and leave it hanging there at the end to make you wonder at the mystery of it.

And there were other stories, too. Like the time she saw a woman buried in ice — or the time she saw a tree walking along the road, its branches filled with a myriad of clouds and its leaves glittering with blue stars. And she thought to herself: "What's a tree doing walking along the road when it could just as easily fly?" For trees could fly when they were not standing still and holding the world together with their roots.

Her technique was simple. The stories were true and they were filled with wonder. Not the kind of wonder that would be understood by an adult, but a child certainly. My Aunt had faith in children, and when she saw one in the street she'd hold out her hand and the child would respond when it might never have responded to another human being.

In my Aunt's mind children were unique. You didn't have to tell them that the world rested on the back of a giant turtle. Any child could see that — and that's why the world wobbled all the time and you had earthquakes and plagues and famine and whooping cough and chicken pox and measles. If it wasn't for the trees, who held the whole thing together with their roots, the world would have collapsed years ago and sunk into an abyss. My Aunt said so. And she was right.

She said the sky wasn't always blue either. It could be any colour you wanted it to be. She once saw a pink sky and she liked it so much she kept it that way for a week in spite of people telling her she was mad. The children didn't think she was mad. The sky belonged to my Aunt — and when she'd finished with it she'd pass it on to them and they could paint it any colour they liked.

When my Aunt wasn't telling stories to children, she made children's clothes and sold them to the neighbours for whatever they could afford. Sometimes, all they could afford was — thanks. But that was all right, too. She'd manage.

And she made dolls — paper dolls from string and newspaper and glue she'd prepared herself. You could see it bubbling in the pot that hung precariously over the fire in the back yard of her house in Evergreen Street. She stood tall. She held a large potstick in her hand and as she stirred the glue I could hear her singing softly to herself — "If I was a witch now, I could change the world". But she wasn't a witch. She was my lone Aunt Bridget. An artist, a storyteller and a lover of children. When she died the sky turned a bright pink and it remained that way for a long time.

19

When my father had an accident on the Quays we thought we were in for a fortune in compensation. Two years later, the compensation arrived — four hundred pounds — most of which he owed to publicans and grocers and solicitors who'd befriended him. With what remained of the compensation, my father decided to go into business. He opened a small coal-store at the bottom of Travers Hill and advertised in the local newspaper: "Coal And Blocks — Delivered Daily To All Parts Of The City". What he omitted to mention was that he had no way of delivering the goods.

"We'll invest in a donkey and cart" he said. "It's the only solution."

He scoured Cork for a suitable donkey and cart and, finally, met a man in a pub who said he had the the ideal thing for sale.

"Is it in good condition?" enquired my father.

"Perfect" replied your man. "The donkey is as strong as a battleship and the cart was made by Chippendale. You can have both for a fiver."

My father handed over the fiver and we were all set to deliver coal and blocks to the citizens of Cork. The donkey, however, had other ideas.

When my father locked him in the stable for the night he kicked the doors down with his hind legs — and then kicked my father and almost crushed him to death against the stable wall.

"He's a bit frisky all right" said my father. But once he starts work he'll be grand. My father was an optimist. The donkey had no intention of starting work. He stood rock solid in the stable yard and kicked anyone who came near him.

"What we need here" my father said — "is an expert".

Cork is full of experts. And Poncho Sullivan was the greatest expert of them all.

"When I was living in the Argentine", he said "sleeping rough on the pampas, you know — I used to watch the Goutshows training wild horses. It's no problem."

71

My father wasn't sure. "This is a donkey" he said — "not a flaming horse."

"Same thing" declared Poncho. "It's entirely a matter of breathing. You approach the animal from the left hand side, breathe gently up its nostrils and it will immediately see how friendly you are."

Poncho did his breathing act and when he was discharged from hospital three weeks later he was on crutches and wore a bandage round his head. "Is it possible" he wrote to his solicitor. "to sue a donkey"? The solicitor never replied. They're like that when it comes to anything simple.

One day, after school, I went along to the coal-store to help my father promote the business of delivering coal and blocks to the citizens of Cork without any means of transport.

The donkey was standing in the yard, daring anyone to come near it, and my father was talking to Pyramid Reilly. He was another expert. He'd studied the pyramids of Egypt for years and could now prove, beyond doubt, that the Lost Tribes of Israel were living in Evergreen Street. He looked at the donkey, examined the shape and the size and the way it was now standing with its rear end facing the sun, and shook his head.

"It's a conundrum" he said.

"I beg your pardon?"

"A puzzle. But I've got the measure of it now. It's not a donkey at all. It's a frustrated racehorse."

"Are you sure"? asked my father.

"Certain declared Pyramid. I won't go into the mathematics of the thing — it would only confuse you. But you've only to look at his behaviour. He's upset. Now, if you were a racehorse and someone tried to pass you off as a donkey, wouldn't you be upset?"

"You have a point there, Pyramid."

"Well there you are then. Take my advice and buy a racing saddle. Put the saddle on his back and go and find yourself a jockey."

My father looked at me and I pleaded for a merciful release. But two days later I was glued to the saddle and the donkey never looked happier. We were now in the racing business. My father sold the coal store, fed the donkey on porter and oats and set me on a diet of onion soup and barley.

"In a week" he said "you'll be thin as a rake and light as a feather. Ideal for a jockey."

I didn't want to be a jockey. I wanted to live in Tibet and be a monk with a bald head and eat goat's meat. I prayed that the donkey might have a stroke. I promised to give up swearing and stop staring at girls and wondering what they looked like under their skirts. I promised anything and everything if only God would put an end to it all. But God wasn't talking to me then. I'd denied Him too often and said He was deaf as a post.

We went into strict training. Two hours in the morning before school. Two hours in the evening after school. The donkey was in his element and I was suffering from nervous exhaustion.

The end came suddenly. I was sitting in the Lee Fields one day, resting my weary bones, and the donkey was eating grass from a small patch near the Lee Road. At the far end of the field a group of boys were playing hurley. I watched the ball rise high in the air and then fall directly on the donkey's head. The effect was miraclous. He reared up on his hind legs, brayed as if he'd swallowed a foghorn and bolted straight down the Lee Road. I followed — slowly — and by the time I reached Washington Street the city was at a standstill. Traffic was held up. Pedestrians were fleeing in all directions — and four policemen, with a rope, were struggling to put the donkey under restraint. By the time my father arrived they had managed to do so.

I glowed with relief. The donkey was dragged on to the back of a lorry and my father was taken to the Bridewell where he was charged with being in possession of a dangerous animal. He was fined ten pounds and ordered to get rid of the beast. The donkey was sold. My racing days were over and I believed in the Holy Spirit for a week.

20

My paternal Grandmother, Lizzie Baron, sat by the window of her room in Mary Street and watched the children playing handball against the side wall of Miss Mac's sweet shop directly opposite. She sat there every day now — ever since my Grandfather died and she had decided not to leave the house anymore. I went to visit her often, but she seldom spoke. She seemed content just to sit there watching the children playing handball and waiting to be reunited with my Grandfather.

"He was a big man" she said. "Biggest man in the world. He was not to be dead."

She paced her words. Measured them out slowly, one at a time, and laid them down before me — a pavement to her mind.

I wanted to know about my Grandfather, I wanted to know where they had met and whether it was true that she was Greek and my Grandfather had rescued her from a band of maurading Turks. But she shrugged her shoulders, as if it were of no consequence, and continued to stare out of the window.

Presently, she said: "He talked to the stones. He wished to be buried in a wall. Your people did not do that. It was not right."

"Do you want to be buried in a wall?"

"I lie with him" she said.

I looked at the room. When my Grandfather was alive it seemed large and airy. Now it was small. The window was open, but the room smelled of old clothes and stale food. In the sink beside her, the unwashed crockery and china plates lay piled high — and on the floor near the fire my Grandfather's boots lay turned on one side as if drying out after a day in the rain. Above the fire, the mantelpiece was bare. She had removed the clock that had stood there for years and now there was no time in the room and the only sound was that of the ball bouncing against the wall across the street.

In a corner of the room, my Grandfather's bed stood as it had always stood — close to the wall and covered with a dark red quilt. But she had made the bed and my Grandfather's nightshirt, neatly ironed, lay folded carefully across two pillows. It was the only task she performed daily. Everything else was unimportant. When I asked her about her past, she said that was unimportant. And when I asked her how she felt now about those who had persecuted her when she had first arrived in the city, she said she had seen worse and so had my Grandfather, but she would not say where and asked me to change the subject. I changed the subject and asked her why my Grandfather wanted to be buried in a wall.

"Did he like walls?"

"No" she said. "He did not like walls." And left it at that.

My mother was right. Trying to get information from Lizzie Baron was like pulling teeth. I tried again.

"If he didn't like walls", I said "why did he want to be buried in one?"

She turned her head. Studied me for a moment and replied - "Stones. There is truth in stones. Can you swim?"

"Swim?"

"Your Grandfather could swim. He was a fine swimmer. I saw him. He rose from the water like a bird. He lay on the sand naked. He was naked in the woods. Always naked. Always beautiful. Not to be dead."

I looked at her face. I had no idea what she was talking about. I couldn't imagine my Grandfather being naked. I had never thought of him as being beautiful and I had never seen him swim.

"Why was he naked?" I asked.

She smiled. And for a moment I thought she was mocking me. But her eyes were sad and when I looked down at her hands they were held tightly together and the knuckles glowed white from pressure and tension.

"Why?" I persisted. But she refused to answer and lowered her head.

I felt guilty then and knew that, somehow, it was wrong to question her. She was struggling for words. She didn't want to answer questions anymore. She had said enough.

"I'm sorry" I said. " I won't ask you again."

She raised her head, paused for a moment, and then moved towards the bed. When she reached the bed, she knelt on the floor beside it and pulled out a tin box from beneath it. She opened the box and withdrew a number of tattered and faded photographs. She handed them to me. They were photographs of walls.

On the ground beside one wall, a group of people lay dead. The wall above them was pockmarked with bullet holes. Against another wall, two children stood facing the camera. They looked puzzled and hungry. A third wall was blank, apart from what appeared to be a list of names scratched along the side in a language I did not understand. A fourth showed a man and a woman standing beside it, holding hands. And the last photograph was of a wall covered with photographs of men, women and children.

The photographs frightened me and I wondered what they meant and why she was showing them to me now. She said nothing and just sat there on the floor watching me as I turned them over and looked at them again.

"The children" I said."Who are they?"

"No questions" she said. "Just look."

I looked at the one showing the man and the woman holding hands. I wanted to ask who they were too, but I knew she wouldn't answer me.

The woman was small. Her eyes stared at the camera and out beyond it to something far off in the distance. She wore dark clothes and her long black hair hung loosely over her shoulders and down to her waist. The man beside her was tall. He was wearing a pair of short trousers. His chest was bare and his feet were bare. He was looking at the woman and in his right hand he carried a revolver.

I turned to the remaining photographs, but my Grandmother stretched out her hand and said — "Give them to me now". I gave her the photographs and she held them in her hand for a moment before replacing them in the tin box and returning the box to its place beneath the bed. Then, she rose to her feet, crossed the room again and resumed her seat near the window.

I sat close beside her and together we watched the children playing in the street.We heard the sound of the ball as it bounced, backwards and forwards, against the side wall of Miss Mac's sweetshop.

21

You could feel the air. And if you stood close to Miss Mac's window in Mary Street you could taste the fruit. It was laid out in long wooden trays and there were apples and oranges and pears and bananas and currants and sultanas and you knew it was Christmas. The cold air rose to a mist and if you held your breath and then let it all out again in one great gush it would cover the window and you could write your name on it. Miss Mac wouldn't be pleased and, sometimes, she'd shout at you — but she tried not to because she knew it was Christmas too and everyone spoke kindly to each other at Christmas.

Miss Mac was kindly. She handed out free bags of sweets to the children and then went to Midnight Mass and sang hymns to the Virgin Mary. The Virgin Mary had a baby in her arms. Miss Mac wanted a baby of her own, but my father said no one would marry her because she had consumption and you couldn't have babies when you had consumption. Other people had consumption too, but at Christmas you didn't think about things like that. You played happy. Everyone played happy. The rich spoke to the poor and a star shone in the South Chapel and the poor didn't feel poor anymore because it was Christmas.

It was Christmas in the kitchen. My mother made the Christmas pudding and said you had to be careful with pudding because it was difficult to make and if you didn't do it properly it could explode all over the place and make holes in the ceiling. My mother was careful. She laid a pillowcase on the table and filled it with fruit and a handful of suet and my father added porter. You could smell the porter.And when the pudding boiled black in in the cast iron pot there was steam everywhere. It penetrated the walls and clung to the rafters and you could feel with the tang on your tongue that now it was Christmas.

You didn't grow at Christmas. You stood perfectly still and your height remained the same and the mist covered time because you wanted everything to stay exactly as it was now and it would always be Christmas.Your father didn't grow either and your mother was young and there were no grey hairs in her head because she'd dyed it with henna. My father dyed his hair too, but would never admit it, though everyone could see because he'd done it with boot polish.

My father drank whiskey at Christmas. He paid twopence for *The Echo* when it only cost a penny because the newsboy deserved a tip and and he knew it was Christmas. My father's friend, Murty, knew it was Christmas too, and my father said he deserved something as well, though he never paid for his drink, but you could forgive that around Christmas.

When my mother saw Murty in the street, she bought him another drink and Murty was drunk and fell all over the place and swore to God and his Holy Mother that he would never touch whiskey again until next Christmas. Then she went to visit Mrs. Barrett, who lived across the street and was sick and bought her a whiskey too because she needed it to kill the germs. Mrs. Barrett was old and some people called her a witch, but at Christmas she changed into an angel.

The city was filled with angels. You could see them in Patrick Street and above the altar in the South Chapel and they all had wings and, sometimes, it snowed. You waited for snow and if the snow failed to arrive you could always buy pretend-snow and sprinkle it on the windows where it glittered and shone and felt cold and them warm and crinkley-toed and blessed with Christmas.

It was Christmas everywhere then. With Maisie Sweeney and me as we sat on the stairs of our tenement house while she read aloud from her book crammed with ghosts and goblins and fairies and things that went scrump in the night. It was Christmas in corners. It lit up the dark and and filled you with light and turned on the stars on a giant Christmas tree.

You believed in ghosts, but you weren't afraid of them because they all ran away at Christmas and you knew you were brave until you were foolish enough to ask Maisie why they had chains on their feet and she told you.

Maisie Sweeney knew all about ghosts, and the reason they had chains on their feet was because they'd forgotten to give presents to children like Maisie Sweeney and now they were suffering the torments of the damned. You would remember Maisie Sweeney and make sure to buy her a present for Christmas and sprinkle it with holy water.

When I told my friend, Connors, about Maisie Sweeney he

said that the only thing she deserved for Christmas was a poisoned apple. He deserved a poisoned apple too, but you couldn't say that because he was your best friend and you never knew what he planned to give you for Christmas. Connors didn't believe in Christmas. He gave his mother a box of chocolates one year and when she opened the box there was an explosion you could hear all over Cork.

I was wedded to Christmas. I sang in the choir at Christmas. And when we arrived back at the house after Midnight Mass in the South Chapel there was porter on the table and a chicken from the chicken factory where my mother worked over the season. She stuffed the chicken. She filled it with breadcrumbs and spoonfulls of sausage-meat and drenched it with porter just to give it soul. I wasn't interested in soul. I was drunk on Razza and bottles of Kia-Ora and my stomach was bubbling with excitement from Christmas.

There'd be presents in the morning. They'd be lying at the foot of my bed and packed in my stocking and there was bound to be a train-track and an apple and a penny and a bag full of sweets.

It was warm by the fire. The night cradled me. And when I woke up in the morning, the room was a golden glow and the day that was in it sang Christmas.

22

Salty O'Cleary was a small whiskery little man who never married because he saw no sense in courting danger. He didn't live in a house either because the walls stifled him and he couldn't see the stars at night. But every Sunday, after church, Salty would visit our house. He'd give a loud knock on the door, step back three paces, and wait for the door to open.

Inside the house, Salty's signal was clearly understood. My mother would disappear into the kitchen and my father would open the door.

"Come in" he'd say. "You're more than welcome." And Salty would reply — "I was only passing."

Salty was always only passing. He never went anywhere directly and never intended stopping off when he arrived. But he'd come inside anyway, peer anxiously around the room, and then head straight for the fireplace. Only then was my mother permitted to leave the kitchen. Salty was safe — his back to the fire — the roaring flames protecting him from women.

"In the old days", Salty declared, "the world was ruled entirely by women and they'd made an awful mess of it. Things were different now, thank God, but you still had to be careful." And when Salty said that he made sure to move closer to the fire and throw another sod of turf on it.

In a distant corner of the room, my mother sat and listened. She thought Salty was great. A little cracked in the head maybe, but a grand story-teller. I never knew what to think and laughed — until Salty put the fear of God in me with tales of the headless coach and the great God Mog, who ate children for breakfast and kept their bones in a bag to feed his four mad Alsatian dogs.

My father, as usual, said little. But when the stories became too outrageous he'd take down his tin whistle from its place above the mantelpiece and play a jig or a reel and everyone would dance — except Salty. He moved closer to the fire. There were far too many women about and he wished to God they'd stay at home and keep the door locked.

Presumably, at some stage in his life, Salty must have had a mother, but he never mentioned her. The idol of his life was his father — and when he died Salty took to the roads. He piled his few meagre belongings on to a handcart, pushed it before him, and swore that he would never live in a house again.

On Summer nights, Salty slept in the fields and during the long winter months he slept in a makeshift tent with a hole in the top so that he could see the stars.He slept alone, avoided all contact with women, and if you asked him why he'd cry — "Disaster!"

Sometimes, Salty would talk of other things besides women — but it didn't last. Like the time he was pushing the handcart along the road and the ground opened up and swallowed him. Salty had often prayed for the ground to open up and swallow him, but he never expected to be taken seriously. When he recovered, he found himself in an open grave. It took him half an hour to climb out and it put years on to him. Salty didn't like graves because you never knew who they'd put on top of you. It could be a woman. When Salty died, he wanted to be buried in a tower with a perpetual fire blazing all round him. Women were afraid of fire. Salty knew that from his father.

When his father was alive, Salty used to ask him about women. He never saw one in the house and when he passed one in the street his father told him to keep his eyes shut. Salty kept his eyes shut and was forever being run over by horses and people riding bicycles along the footpath. His father said women were a screed. You couldn't be up to them. If you looked at them crooked they'd poison you. And if you looked at them straight they'd read you and you'd fall over yourself and break a leg.

"Best not to look at all" said his father. "Keep well away from them." And Salty did — and his father nurtured him.

Salty had faith in his father and when his father told him that he had once had the misfortune to marry a woman, Salty asked him what happened to her. But his father wouldn't tell him — "It would only upset you" he said. And Salty was grateful for that because he really didn't want to know about his mother.

He was happy with his father. They went for walks in the country. They went fishing down the Marina. And, in the evenings, they sat by the fire and his father told him stories.

The stories were about men. Good men. Decent men — and how they were all plagued by the hauntings of women. Salty

84

listened. He didn't know that his father had killed his mother. He didn't know that his mother lay in an unmarked grave in another part of the country. He moved closer to the fire. The shadows lengthened across the room and his father held him.

The last time I saw Salty he was pushing the handcart before him along a country road in West Cork. It was a warm summer's day, but Salty was dressed in a long black heavy overcoat and, for the first time in his life, he was wearing a hat. He looked old and tired. And when I asked him where he was going he said — "Nowhere. I'm only passing." I wished him luck and he moved on. I never saw him again.

23

Paul Muni was appearing in "Black Fury" at the Savoy cinema and my mother said he was the greatest actor in the world and Black Fury was the best film ever made. It was also the only film she'd seen, so her judgement was crucial. I was determined to see it.

My father, however, had turned against the cinema. He said it was a corrupting influence, invented by Lenin to confuse the people of Cork. When my mother suggested it was time he consulted a doctor, my father went down on his knees and offered up The Rosary for the salvation of her soul. Then he went to Mass.

He went to Mass twice a day now — ever since he saw God in his cups and gave up the drink and turned to religion. He had the house consecrated to the Sacred Heart, he offered up novenas for the conversion of Russia, and on Sundays he played hymns on the tin whistle when he should have been playing jigs and reels. He was also convinced that he'd seen a burning bush in the back yard, but by the time he'd reached it the bush had disappeared. I was praying that my father would disappear so that I could go to the Savoy cinema and see Paul Muni.

Paul Muni was a star. The Savoy cinema shone with stars. They were built into the ceiling and when the lights were dimmed the stars twinkled above your head and heaven was only an ice-cream away.

Fred Bridgeman was a star. He played the organ. He sat at the keyboard in full evening dress, and the organ rose from the ground through a fountain of light, and the words of the songs appeared on the screen and we all sang "Mexicali Rose" and tried to sound like Gene Autry. My father wouldn't appreciate things like that. He was too busy talking to God — though the only films God ever appeared in were diabolical.

On Sunday afternoons, when the neighbours had departed with the music of Mother Of Mercy still ringing in their ears, my father retired to bed. My mother went to visit her mother's grave in Douglas and I sat cross-legged on the kitchen floor dreaming of the stars. On this particular Sunday, I was dreaming of Paul Muni.

Earlier in the day, I did happen to mention to my father that I wanted to go to the pictures to see Mr. Muni and he replied, with his usual breathtaking clarity, "I'll give you bloody pictures!" and then retreated to the bedroom. It's at moments like that that you begin to wonder how anyone ever manages to understand the English language. He removed my shoes too, and planked them under his pillow. "You won't go far without shoes" he said. "Not on a Sunday anyway."

Sunday was important in Cork. On any other day of the week you could walk the streets of the city in your bare feet and no one would notice. Sunday was different. That's because it was God's Day and God had a fetish about shoes. He wanted everyone to wear them. My father said that — and he knew. He was now in direct communication with God and God told him everything.

You could feel sorry for my father. He'd forgotten I was an atheist and didn't give a hang about shoes. My only interest was the cinema. And while my father slept, I opened the front door, and ten minutes later I was standing in the queue outside the Savoy cinema. A few committed Christians stared at my bare feet and a number of others made some disparaging remarks about the effects of the Russian Revolution on the children of Cork — but I stood firm. I was now a dedicated atheist and I did not have to wear shoes on Sunday. I read that in a book.

I had just about reached the head of the queue when my father appeared waving an ash-plant above his head. Anyone could see he wasn't happy and before I knew where I was he was all over me shouting, "The curse o' God on ye — and that fella Muni, too! I'll anoint the both of ye!" There was no point hanging around listening to that kind of talk, so I ran.

My father chased me across Patrick Street — up Winthrop Street -and I had just managed to reach the Post Office in Oliver Plunkett Street when I ran straight into Mugsy Corrigan. He was from the North Side and was reputed to be a boxer,but he'd never met my father and he hadn't a notion of who I was. When I ran into him he almost had a stroke.

"Oh!" he cried — raising me three feet in the air by the scruff of the neck — "Oh! And what the Hell do you think you're doing, ye thick?"

I was about to offer a perfectly reasonable explanation when my father arrived on the scene.

"Let me at him!" he roared. "Just let me get me two hands on him!"

"Control yourself" said Mugsy. "Control yourself! What's the matter with ye? Sure he's only a child."

"A child? What child? He's me own son, isn't he?"

Mugsy looked at me. "Is that thing your father?" he asked. And may Paul Muni forgive me, but I took one look at the ash-plant and denied everything.

"I don't know who he is" I said. "He's been following me all day."

My father choked. Mugsy turned pale, lowered me gently to the ground and placed a protective arm round my shoulder. He glared at my father.

"You ought to be ashamed of yourself he said. An old goat like you, chasing little boys."

That was too much for my father. He removed his jacket, laid it carefully down on the pavement, and then tried to split Mugsy over the head with the ash-plant. Mugsy retaliated by punching my father on the jaw, and before you could say trapstick or Nobbling Thomas a crowd had gathered and Mugsy and my father were battling it out in front of the Post Office.

By the time the police arrived, my father's shirt had been torn to ribbons and some committed Christian had stolen his jacket. He was not amused. And while the crowd were regarding Mugsy as the hero of the day, my father was bundled into a police van and driven off to the Bridewell. I watched from a distance — and then ran all the way home and hid under the bed.

Three days later, my father was released from jail and I developed a severe dose of flu when I heard he was coming home. He arrived wearing a borrowed shirt. My mother made him a cup of tea. She made me a cup of tea. We sat by the table — and the silence was deafening.

24

My cousin, Beatrice, was fish. She never married. And for thirty-one years she sat by her stall in the Coal Quay Market and sold fish. She sold mackerel and herring, pollack and hake, whitefish and crabfish, salmon and skate. My cousin Beatrice slept with fish. And when she woke up in the mornings the scales clung to her.

"Is it any wonder I never married? I belong with fish."

My cousin, Beatrice, talked of fish. And the room she lived in at the corner of Grattan Street was an ocean of fish. She spoke with fish. She knew them by name and by stream — and when their seasons came and the fish gathered in shoals along the River Lee — she sang with fish.

"Is it any wonder the world envies me? I sing with fish."

My cousin, Beatrice, dreamed of fish. She knew where they lived — in sunken castles a thousand fathoms deep -and in her dreams she'd visit them.The sharks pleasured her. The whales carried her on their backs and the salmon waltzed with her.

"Is it any wonder the people persecute me? I dance with fish."

But one morning my cousin, Beatrice, awoke from her dreams and knew that she hated fish. The hate grew on her breast. A dark stream weeping through her skin. She could see it in the mirror. She could smell the stench. She could hear the sea rising through a green mist to cover her.

"Is it any wonder the sea haunts me? I drown in fish."

My cousin, Beatrice, rose from her stall in the Coal Quay Market and renounced fish. She bought perfumes and herbs, ointments and soaps, and a wire brush to scrub herself clean. But the stench remained. She could feel it under her fingernails and on her hands. She could taste it in her mouth and her clothes reeked of it.

She burned her clothes. She removed the bedclothes from the bed and she burned them, too. She opened the window of her room and screamed out at the people in Grattan Street —

"People of Cork — I abjure all fish."

91

My cousin, Beatrice, grew nightmares of fish. She sat in a courtroom surrounded by fish. The judge was a fish. The prosecuting council was a fish. And the jury, stretched out like sardines in a tin, were all fish.

She was accused of slaughtering fish and selling their bodies for profit on the Coal Quay Market. She pleaded for mercy. She said the fish were already dead when she received them. She said she was only a poor woman struggling hard to make a living. And she asked what was the harm now in selling dead fish?

"But you can't argue with fish. They stood on their tails and said I'd murdered their fathers and their mothers and the pride of their unborn children. The sweat stood out on me like beads of glass and I woke up screaming."

My cousin, Beatrice, became fish. The doctors said so and they pointed out how she gulped in the air through her sides and wriggled on the floor when the nightmares were over. They wrapped her in a canvas bag filled with sea-water. They fed her on food fit only for fish. And when she wept they comforted her.

"Is it any wonder the fish tortured me? I abandoned fish".

My cousin, Beatrice, was fish. And when her season was over the sea opened in waves and treasured her remains.

25

It was one of those long blue and lazy afternoons in Autumn and along the Mardyke the trees were shedding their leaves for the last time in his life. Mr. Goldman knew it would be the last time and he said so without rancour or regret.

"I grow old" he said. "What else is there for me to do but to die gracefully."

"Are you a hundred?" I asked.

"Maybe two" he replied. "And you?"

"I'll be twelve in August."

"You're growing old too," he said. "Soon now, you'll be as old as I am."

We sat on the park bench and watched the leaves falling from the trees. They formed a glittering golden scatter along the pathway and he said :

"You'd never think to look at them now that they were once green and springing." He shook his head, opened his newspaper carefully and stared at the headlines. I could tell he was old. The grey lines of his time wrinkled his forehead and the brown spots on his hands mirrored his days. He read the small print with a magnifying glass and I could almost hear his bones creak.

"They're dying in Madrid" he said. "It'll be over soon. Have you been to school to-day?"

"No."

"Mitching again? You should go to school. You might learn something there. I can't teach you everything."

"You've taught me a lot."

"Maybe. But there's always something more."

"Like what?"

"I don't know. But something."

He folded his newspaper with extreme care and raised his head. I could see the tears in his eyes.

"The important thing" he said — and paused. "The important thing now is to know what's happening in the world. The

Spaniards know about things like that. Would you like to go to Madrid?"

"Would you?"

"I'm too old. I was even too old when the war started. But I should have tried to go anyway instead of standing at street corners protesting. That's easy."

"You did what you could."

"Maybe. But it's too late now anyway. Franco will be in Madrid in no time at all."

"My father says the war will be over then."

"And what does your mother say?"

"She thinks there'll be an even bigger war later on."

"She's probably right. Let's go for a walk."

He placed the folded newspaper inside his overcoat pocket and held me by the hand. We walked towards the bandstand.

"Sometimes" he said "they play some wonderful music there. It fills the air. Do you like music?"

"Yes. People come to our house every Sunday and play music all the time."

"Of course. I'd forgotten that. It's a nice custom."

He paused. Leaned against the bandstand and said: "You know, when I was in Spain, many years ago, I used to sit in the cafes every night and listen to the Spaniards playing the music of their lives. I don't suppose they're playing a great deal of music now."

"Do you like the Spaniards?"

"Very much. They're a remarkable people."

The bandstand was closed. There would be no music that day. Not until the weekend. It was not a holiday. A number of unemployed dockers were lying on the grass enjoying the afternoon sun and a group of children were playing Rounders close to the Western Road.

"One of these days there'll be an accident there", he said. "It's too close to the road. Do you want to go home now?"

"I think so. I feel sad to-day, for some reason."

"Me, too. Try and go to school to-morrow. Perhaps I'll see you afterwards. It's a pity about the music."

"Yes."

He turned away and I watched him walking slowly back towards the park bench. When he reached the bench he sat down again and removed the folded newspaper from his overcoat pocket. He looked at the headlines, studied the small print with the aid of a magnifying glass and wiped his eyes with a clean handkerchief. He moved on. V*iva La Quince Brigada*, old stock. *Viva La Quince Brigada.*

26

Chrissie Watson wasn't bad
She gave her husband all she had
But when she saw he wasn't dead
She cut his throat and went to bed.

Chrissie Watson lived in Blue Boy's Lane and everyone said she
was a demon because when her husband died she refused to
attend the funeral and looked ten years younger the following
day when she went to collect on his Insurance Policy.

"The curse of God on them!" said Chrissie. "After forty years
of marriage I deserve ten Insurance Policies."

Chrissie's son, Michael, didn't attend the funeral either, but
that was because Chrissie locked him in the cupboard and said
she'd only let him out if he promised to dance on his father's
grave. Michael managed to escape through the back window,
but by the time he reached the graveyard the funeral was over
and his father was under six feet of clay.

"I tried me best" he told his father. "But you know what she's
like."

"I do indeed" replied his father. "May she fall in a ditch."

"Are you comfortable down there?" Michael asked him.

"I am not!" his father moaned. "Did you see the coffin she
bought me? She must have got that in a secondhand shop."

"I'm sorry, Da. But she wouldn't spend the money. I'll bring
you flowers to-morrow."

"You'll do nothing of the kind! Haven't I enough to contend
with without you sticking flowers all over me? Go home to your
bed."

"Yes, Da."

"You're a good boy — but you have no bloody sense."

"I know that, Da. But can I come back and talk to you
sometimes?"

"You can if you want to. I'll hardly be moving house."

"That's true, Da. Good-night, so."

"Good-night! And mind yourself on the way home. That

97

mother of yours may have put a curse on you."

Michael walked sideways from the graveyard and kept his fingers crossed all the way home in case Chrissie had put a curse on him.

When Michael was young, his mother was always putting curses on him. "And when I criticized her one time she caught hold of me tongue and for weeks afterwards I couldn't speak or pass water." Michael gave up criticizing after that and spent most of his time wandering around graveyards and sleeping rough under headstones.

"You'll catch your death of cold out there" said Chrissie. "Are you demented, or what?"

"I like graveyards" Michael replied." I feel safe out there."

"Safe? You're thirty-eight years of age. Can't you think of something better to do?"

"I talk to me Da."

"And does he answer you?"

"He does, Ma."

Chrissie shook her head. "I always knew there was a knot in your brain. Get into the cupboard."

And Michael entered the cupboard and Chrissie locked the door on him and he sat there in the dark thinking about his father.

One day, when Michael arrived home from the graveyard, where he had been sleeping rough beside his father's grave, he found his mother in what he described as her witch's mood. He wasn't sure what he meant by that, but she was very solicitous. She'd baked him a cake. She made him some tea and she hovered about him, tending to his every need, as if he were an invalid and expected to die at any minute. And, true enough, he didn't feel at all well after drinking the tea. His mother, on the other hand, never looked better — but he only noticed that as he was leaving the house.

"You're going now?" she asked.

"I am" replied Michael.

"And may I enquire where you're going?"

"You may. I'm going to visit me Da's grave."

"That's a good boy" said Chrissie. "He could do with the company."

Michael left the house and walked slowly towards the cemetery. When he reached his father's grave, he sat on the gravestone and spoke to his father.

"She was very good to me to-day", he said. "Best ever."

"Oh, yes?" groaned his father. "Kind, was she?"

"Yes, Da. Falling over me with kindness. she was."

"That's a bad sign" said his father. "She was kind to me, too. Now look at me".

"Did she poison you , Da?"

"She did that. And then tried to cut the head off me with a knife."

"Maybe it was an accident, Da."

"Accident be damned! I was in mortal agony. How do you feel?"

"Queezy, Da".

"Queezy? I thought as much. The Lord help you. You'll be joining me soon."

Michael rose to his feet and resolved to sleep in the graveyard that night and every night from now on.

It was a week later when the Parish Priest found Michael lying face down on his father's grave.It had been raining steadily over the past few days and Michael was now suffering from pneumonia. The Parish Priest called for an ambulance and Michael was removed to the South Infirmary, where he died two days later.

When Chrissie heard the news she said she was devastated, and on the day of the funeral she retired to bed and refused to leave it. She said she was ill and would never be the same again.

It was my father who attended to the funeral arrangements and it was our next door neighbours who carried Michael's coffin to the grave. He was greeted by his father.

"Didn't I say you were done for?" his father said. "Didn't I warn you?"

"You did, Da. She's done for us both now."

"Move close beside me, like a good boy. We'll haunt her together."

"I'd prefer to do it meself, Da."

"Well, if that's what you want. But do it properely. There's no point in employing half measures."

On their way home from the graveyard, my father said he saw Michael's ghost coming from the direction of Chrissie's house. His friend, Murty, was convinced he'd seen it too. If it

Patrick Galvin

wasn't him he said — it was the dead spit of him. My father
suggested keeping the news to themselves — for the time being
anyway.

When they arrived at Chrissie's house they found the front
door open and when they entered the kitchen they found
Chrissie lying on the floor with her mouth open and a look of
horror on her face. They carried her to the bedroom and Murty
went to fetch a doctor. Presently, Chrissie opened her eyes.

"Did you see him?" she asked my father.

"Who?"

"Michael. I was lying on the bed and I heard the front door
opening below. He called out to me, but by the time I got
downstairs he'd gone."

"Did he say anything?"

"He said I'd killed him. He said I'd killed his father, too. Me!
His own mother. How could I do a thing like that?"

When the doctor arrived my father left the house and
Chrissie fell into a deep sleep from which she never recovered.
She was buried between her husband and her son. There were
no mourners.

27

A dark-haired woman arrived at our front door one day and offered to read my fortune if I crossed her palm with silver. I didn't have any silver and offered her the top of a lemonade bottle instead. She said I'd die of drowning. Three weeks later I fell into the River Lee near Parnell Bridge and had to be rescued by my friend Connors.

"That's the second time you tried to drown yourself" he said. "This could get monotonous."

Connors didn't know about the fortune-teller — and when I told him he said she was a cloth-head. "And you're worse for believing her. I thought you said you were an atheist?"

"I am."

"Then next time she calls give her a cup of tea and put weed-killer in it. That's what I would have done."

"You would not."

"I would so!"

And you could believe Connors. He had faith in weed-killer and regarded all fortune-tellers as lunatics who ought to be put down.

I wasn't sure about fortune-tellers.And when I asked my mother about them she said some people were gifted with second sight and you had to accept that — though she herself had never been to visit one and neither had my father. He believed in cats.

If he saw a black cat on the road, he knew it was going to rain. If he saw a white cat at the front door he was sure there was going to be a war. Sometimes he was right. Sometimes it rained. And, sometimes, the war fell on us here.

On our side of the city there were few cats, but the fortune-tellers prospered, though their predictions were limited. They never forecast the ending of the world or the dawning of a new Ice Age — and they seldom committed themselves to anything beyond the misery of hope. They charged a shilling for that and an extra sixpence for whatever personal future you were desperate to secure.

If you were an unmarried woman — then all you needed was a man. If you were a married woman — all you required was faith and the prospect of a constant job for himself in Dunlops or Fords. The crystal ball would take care of that. The Tarot cards would chart the course and the tea leaves would reveal the day and the hour when the postman would arrive with a special letter. When that special letter failed to arrive — well, you could hardly blame the tea leaves for that. Perhaps your faith wasn't strong enough or the light was bad. "Shall we try again, dear?"

And why not. We thrive on hopelessness and witness in the lifeline of our hand the poverty and ignorance of our times.

Sometimes, of course, the fortune-tellers of Cork aspired to be healers or doctors and, in truth, perhaps they were. Is your asthma bad? Is there consumption in the house? A bereavement in your life or a broken dream? You stand outside the Penny Dinner House in Hanover Street and you count your dreams. You haven't got them anymore. You haven't a shirt to your back or a shawl to wrap round you and the shame consumes you. Can a fortune-teller cure that? She can — and more. She can hold your hand and, like the leper of old, you'll be grateful for a human touch.

And, I suppose, in a way, that's what it's all about. We gaze into our crystal ball and we search for the light.

"Carry it with you dear. It will see you through. The pain will go." And sometimes it does. But only sometimes.

When I was growing wild in Cork, the city was filled with dreams and poverty abounded. It clung to the walls of tenement houses. It pervaded the streets. It was etched into the bones of children and adults and it conquered the spirit and aspirations of men.We needed our dreams and we cried out to our fortune-tellers — for who else could provide a future at the turn of a card?

There was Toesy Hanlon from Cove Street. She sat in her bare feet and touched the sick, the blind and the maimed with her left foot and they felt better for it. She counselled the poor, provided new dreams and rich futures, read tea leaves for the girls, and saw her own death revealed in the bottom of a cup. She raised her prices after that because she hadn't long to go. But she lived to be a hundred and died rich — and nobody blamed her because that was her way and she had brought them hope.

The Stanley sisters also provided hope. They worked in tandem and never left a client without some light in the darkness.

"The man who loves you is married, dear — but the wife is not well. We'll offer up a novena." And so they did.

But best of all was Nostra Keegan. She sat in a heap in her tent — held fast to her crytstal ball — and offered nothing but the truth. She said Fords and Dunlops would soon be no more. She said the quays would lie black, the dole queues would lengthen and there would be a great war which would engulf us all.

I won't be around to see it, dear, but it's misty in the ball. "Have you tried emigrating — or a holiday in Bermuda?"

We tried emigrating. Nostra remained at home — and when she died they carried her to the cemetery in Douglas, still clutching her crystal ball.

"I may not need it up there, dear, but it's as well to be prepared."

Nostra was always prepared and raised her umbrella long before it rained.

I could believe in Nostra. I could believe in all the fortune-tellers and all the clairvoyants and I was born when Pluto was in conjunction with Mars. What more did I need? Connors would have said — "Weed-killer." But I wasn't sure about that. For the poverty remained. And darkly darkly sang the tenements of Cork.

28

If you looked closely at the face of the clock, standing on the mantelpiece in our house in Margaret Street, you would see that it was made by Hilser's of Cork. And if you opened the sideboard drawer, set in the kitchen, you would see a small box with a broken hinge. The box belonged to my mother. She treasured the contents — and if you were brave enough to open the box you would discover a dark brown medal bearing the following inscription: *Seachtain Na Casca — 1916*. On the lining of the box you would see the name of the jeweller who supplied it — M. Roche, 61 Patrick Street, Cork.

Sometimes, on those long Sunday afternoons when my father had retired to bed and my mother had gone to visit her mother's grave in Douglas, I wondered about that box. Where had it come from? Who was the medal presented to and for what service? But when I asked my mother about it she would say "It's a long time ago. Leave it now." And I would leave it there, locked in a drawer, safe among shadows.

When you are very young, shadows have meaning and their substance fills you. Stretch out your hand and you can feel the flesh. Probe deeper and you touch grieving bone. When you look at the clock, the hands tell you nothing. Only the shadows are real — and a small box with a broken hinge.

When my mother returned from the graveyard that day her hands were stained with earth and moss and her skirt was damp from kneeling on wet grass.

"I was cleaning the headstone" she said. "I planted some flowers, too. The old ones are dead. It looks better now."

"Does it?"

"Much better. Will you promise me something?"

"If I can."

"When I die — bury me beside my mother."

It's hard to think of your mother being dead. She wears a black shawl, fringed and tassled and she will live forever. But when you look at her face now you can see the years and you know that she is not the same woman who suckled you when

105

young. You're still young. You're twelve years of age, but you feel older and the years weigh on you.

There was a time when I didn't feel like that. I sat high on my father's shoulders and he carried me into the English Market and down the Marina and I felt a thousand years young and filled with expectation. When we arrived home my mother would be there. She'd be baking a cake or washing the clothes or cleaning the house and, sometimes, she'd be painting slogans on the walls. She didn't do that anymore. She went to her mother's grave, laid flowers on the earth, and when she returned home she sat by the fire and counted her beads.

"You're growing up now" she said. "You must learn to take care of yourself. I can't do it anymore."

She shivered with cold, pulled her shawl tightly around her shoulders and let the beads fall silently on to her lap.

"You've let the fire go out" she complained. "You're as bad as your father."

I raked the fire, nursed it with sticks, and covered the flame with a handfull of turf. I sat beside her.

"The medal in the drawer" I said. "Why don't you tell me about it? Who does it belong to?" She shook her head, moved closer to the fire and warmed her hands.

Through the bedroom door I could hear my father beginning to wake up.

"You'd better make him some tea" she said. "You know what he's like at this time of the day."

I filled the kettle, settled it carefully on rising fire, and waited for the water to boil.

When my father entered the room I made the tea and offered them both a cup. My mother refused, but my father accepted and, with the cup in his hand, he moved over to the window and stood there looking down on to the street. Presently, he said :

"In India — I was some champion." He paused for a moment, sipped his tea, and repeated — "Some champion."

My mother ignored him.His photograph stood on the dresser in the kitchen and it was framed in gilt. He wore a British Army uniform and he held a rifle in his hand.

"It's been ages now" he mused" but the Ganges filled me."

My father was a big man and when he walked up Mary Street and Margaret Street the neighbourhood children danced in his wake and called him Gianty. He didn't mind about that. He was proud of his figure, proud of his past and felt the name suited him.

"Six foot four," he said "and no stooper."

My mother stared into the fire and continued to ignore him.

In the bedroom, where they both slept on a large double bed that shaped the room, there were two photographs. One of James Connolly and another of Padraig Pearse.

"They were both shot" my mother said. "Murdered by the British. I want you to remember that." I promised to remember it.

"In India" my father said — "the natives burned their dead."

His photograph stood on the dresser in the kitchen and the rifle bore the legend — Lee Enfield. Point 303. Standard issue.

He turned from the window and looked at my mother." The Ganges" he said "is a holy river. I washed my face in it."

"So you did" said my mother. And rose from her seat beside the fire. She entered the bedroom and the door closed firmly behind her.

"I was some champion!" my father said. "Some champion. Remember that, too. "

I lit the lamp. The room was silent. I was twelve years old and the world was ending.

29

On an evening shortly after my mother's death, my father knelt on the floor of the bedroom they had shared throughout their married life and prayed for her soul. Her photograph stood on the table beside the bed. Her shoes, recently polished, lay under the bed, and her black shawl still hung from a nail behind the bedroom door.

When my father had finished praying for my mother, he rose to his feet and stood for a moment looking down at the white mourning-sheet now stretched across the bed. He had made the bed. He had swept the floor and moved all his personal belongings into a small room at the rear of the house. Nothing more remained to be done. My mother was dead. My father left the room, locked the door securely behind him and never entered the bedroom again.

Six months later, my father moved his belongings from the room at the rear of the house into the kitchen. He locked the back door, slept near the kitchen fire and, like his mother before him, refused to leave the house.

"It will see me out" he said. "We were married here. She died here. It will see me out."

He sat by the fire, close to the bed, his personal belongings scattered about him.

"She left the rosary beads to you" he continued. "I don't know why. Sure you don't believe in anything."

"I'd still like to have them" I said.

"They're hanging on the wall. You can have that tin whistle, too. I don't play it anymore."

"I'm sorry to hear that."

"Nothing to be sorry about. Everything goes in the end."

He reached up and removed the tin whistle from its place above the mantelpiece. It was covered in dust.

"I haven't cleaned it. I haven't cleaned anything in here. Mrs. Barratt comes in sometimes, but you know what she's like."

He handed me the tin whistle and moved closer to the fire. On the dresser beside him, his photograph, framed in gilt, was also covered in dust.

"You can have that, if you want to" he said. "There's nothing else I can give you."

His image smiled through the dust on the photograph and, in his British Army uniform, he looked brave and soldierly.

"India blest me" he said. "Did I tell you that? Reached down to my soul and blest me. Your mother didn't understand that."

"She married you."

"We married each other", he said and lapsed into silence.

Presently, he rose to his feet and moved over to the sideboard. He opened the drawer and removed a small box with a broken hinge. He raised the lid and stared down at the medal resting inside.

"You'd better have that, too" he said. "It belonged to her brother."

"I didn't know she had a brother" I said. "What happened to him?"

My father looked at me for a moment and handed me the box. "He died in jail" he said." What else would you expect?"

He turned away, moved over to the bed and sat on the edge of it. I read the inscription on the medal: *Seachtain Na Casca* — "Politics" he said. "Politics and rememberance. They bleed us dry".

"You had the two days" I said.

"Yes. We had the two days. And I'm grateful for that. Maybe we'll have two more in the next world. I pray we do. But you don't believe in things like that, do you?"

"I'll hang on to the medal." I said.

"And the other things? The photograph, the rosary beads and my tin whistle?"

"Those, too."

"You're odd" he said. "I said that on the day you were born. You haven't changed. Your mother was the same. Odd as bedamned — and a champion of lost causes."

"You were some champion yourself" I said.

"Yes, wasn't I? Some champion. And I washed my face in the Ganges. Not many can say that."

"Not many."

He lowered his head,covered his face with his hands and remained there for a little while, waiting for the dark.

POSTSCRIPT

Once upon a time, in the city of Cork, a famous battle took place. It became known as The Wonderful Battle Of The Starlings. On a bright day, a very bright day with the sun dancing in the sky, the starlings gathered over the city and fought each other for possession of the people of Cork. The battle lasted three days and three nights, and when it was over the streets of the city were covered with the dead bodies of millions of starlings.

Then, mysterious fires broke out. The wooden houses of the Marsh caught fire and the city of Cork was burned to the ground. But the people of Cork rebuilt their city — a capital city which now stands on the banks of the river Lee. Here I was born to evening music and the sound of traffic moving through the streets.